Climate Change

ISSUES
(previously Issues for the Nineties)

Volume 28

Editor

Craig Donnellan

Independence
Educational Publishers
Cambridge

First published by Independence
PO Box 295
Cambridge CB1 3XP
England

British Library Cataloguing in Publication Data
Climate Change – (Issues Series)
I. Donnellan, Craig II. Series
551.6

ISBN 1 86168 057 0

Printed in Great Britain
City Print Ltd
Milton Keynes

Typeset by
Claire Boyd

Cover
The illustration on the front cover is by
The Attic Publishing Co.

CONTENTS

Introduction

Climate Change is the twenty-eighth volume in the series: **Issues**. The aim of this series is to offer up-to-date information about important issues in our world.

Climate Change looks at the causes and effects of global warming.

The information comes from a wide variety of sources and includes:
Government reports and statistics
Newspaper reports and features
Magazine articles and surveys
Literature from lobby groups
and charitable organisations.

It is hoped that, as you read about the many aspects of the issues explored in this book, you will critically evaluate the information presented. It is important that you decide whether you are being presented with facts or opinions. Does the writer give a biased or an unbiased report? If an opinion is being expressed, do you agree with the writer?

Climate Change offers a useful starting-point for those who need convenient access to information about the many issues involved. However, it is only a starting-point. At the back of the book is a list of organisations which you may want to contact for further information.

*****

INTRODUCTION

An introduction to climate change

Information from the Information Unit for Conventions (IUC), UNEP

- Human activities are releasing greenhouse gases into the atmosphere. Carbon dioxide is produced when fossil fuels are used to generate energy and when forests are cut down and burned. Methane and nitrous oxide are emitted from agricultural activities, changes in land use, and other sources. Hydroflurocarbons (HFCs), perfluorocarbons (PFCs), sulphur hexafluoride (SF_6), and other long-lived gases are released by industrial processes. Ozone in the lower atmosphere is generated indirectly by automobile exhaust fumes.

- Rising levels of greenhouse gases are expected to cause climate change. By absorbing infrared radiation, these gases control the flow of natural energy through the climate system. The climate must somehow adjust to the 'thicker blanket' of greenhouse gases in order to maintain the balance between energy arriving from the sun and energy escaping back into space.

- Climate models predict that the global temperature will rise by about 1-3.5°C by the year 2100. This projected change is larger than any climate change experienced over the last 10,000 years. It is based on current emissions trends and assumes that no efforts are made to limit greenhouse gas emissions. There are many uncertainties about the scale and impacts of climate change, particularly at the regional level. Because of the delaying effect of the oceans, surface temperatures do not respond immediately to green-

house gas emissions, so climate change will continue for many decades after atmospheric concentrations have stabilised. Meanwhile, the balance of the evidence suggests that the climate may have already started responding to past emissions.

- Climate change is likely to have a significant impact on the global environment. In general, the faster the climate changes, the greater will be the risk of damage. The mean sea level is expected to rise 15-95 cm by the year 2100, causing flooding of low-lying areas and other damage. Climatic zones (and thus ecosystems and agricultural zones) could shift towards the poles by 150-550 km in the mid-latitude regions. Forests, deserts, rangelands, and other unmanaged ecosystems would face new climatic stresses.

As a result, many will decline or fragment, and individual species will become extinct.

- Human society will face new risks and pressures. Food security is unlikely to be threatened at the global level, but some regions are likely to experience food shortages and hunger. Water resources will be affected as precipitation and evaporation patterns change around the world. Physical infrastructure may be damaged, particularly by sea-level rise and by extreme weather events. Economic activities, human settlements, and human health will experience many direct and indirect effects. The poor and disadvantaged are the most vulnerable to the negative consequences of climate change.

- People and ecosystems will need to adapt to future climatic

1

regimes. Past and current emissions have already committed the earth to some degree of climate change in the 21st century. Adapting to these effects will require a good understanding of socio-economic and natural systems, their sensitivity to climate change, and their inherent ability to adapt. Many strategies are available for adapting to the expected effects of climate change.

- Stabilising atmospheric concentrations of greenhouse gases will demand a major effort. Based on current trends, the total climatic impact of rising greenhouse gas levels will be equal to that caused by a doubling of pre-industrial CO_2 concentrations by 2030, and a trebling or more by 2100. Freezing global CO_2 emissions at their current levels would postpone CO_2-doubling to 2100. Emissions would eventually have to fall to about 30% of their current levels for concentrations to stabilise at doubled-CO_2 levels sometime in the future. Given an expanding world economy and growing populations, this would require dramatic improvements in energy efficiency and fundamental changes in other economic sectors.

- The international community is tackling this challenge through the Climate Change Convention. Adopted in 1992 and now boasting over 170 members, the Convention seeks to stabilise atmospheric concentrations of greenhouse gases at safe levels. It commits developed countries to take measures aimed at returning their emissions, gather relevant information, develop strategies for adapting to climate change, and cooperate on research.

- The 1997 Kyoto Protocol will require stronger action in the post-2000 period. The Parties to the Convention have agreed by consensus on a legally binding commitment for developed countries to reduce their total emissions of six greenhouse gases by at least 5% compared to 1990 levels by the period 2008-2012. The Protocol also establishes an

The main culprits

The graph below shows the percentage of the world's total CO_2 emissions produced by each country versus the percentage of the population of the countries of the world total

	CO₂ emissions % of world's total, 1996	Population % of world's total, 1996
US	25.0	4.7
Europe (inc. E Europe)	19.6	9.0
China	13.5	21.5
Former Soviet Union	10.2	5.0
Japan	5.6	2.2
India	3.6	16.3
UK	2.5	1.02
Republic of Korea	2.2	0.8
Canada	2.1	0.5
Australia	1.3	0.3

Source: World Energy Council and DTI, 1995

emissions trading regime and a 'clean development fund'. It will probably take several years for the Protocol to enter into force.

- Many options for limiting emissions are available in the short and medium term. Policymakers can encourage energy efficiency and other climate-friendly trends in both the supply and consumption of energy. Key consumers of energy include industries, homes, offices, vehicles, and farms. Efficiency can be improved in large part by providing an appropriate economic and regulatory framework for consumers and investors. This framework should promote cost-effective actions, the best current and future technologies, and 'no regrets' solutions that make economic and environmental sense irrespective of climate change. Taxes, regulatory standards, tradable emissions permits, information programmes, voluntary programmes, and the phase-out of counter-productive subsidies can all play a role. Changes in practices and lifestyles, from better urban transport planning to personal habits such as turning out the lights, are also important.

- Energy efficiency gains of 10-30% above baseline trends can be realised over the next 20-30 years at no net cost. Some researchers believe that much greater gains are also feasible during this period and beyond. Improvements over the baseline can be achieved in all major economic sectors with current knowledge and with today's best technologies. In the longer term, it will be possible to move close to a zero-emissions industrial economy – with the innumerable environmental and economic benefits that this implies.

- Reducing uncertainties about climate change, its impacts, and the costs of various response options is vital. In the meantime, it will be necessary to balance concerns about risks and damages with concerns about economic development. The prudent response to climate change, therefore, is to adopt a portfolio of actions aimed at controlling emissions, adapting to impacts, and encouraging scientific, technological, and socio-economic research.

© *Information Unit for Conventions (IUC), UNEP*

Key findings

- The warmest year since the credible global temperature series began in 1860 was 1995, 1997 will be close to this record.
- Analyses of changing patterns of temperature, both at the surface and in the atmosphere, build on the conclusions on attribution in the IPCC 1995 Second Assessment Report, and strengthen the view that human activities have already altered global climate.
- The Hadley Centre model predicts a global warming of about 3°C over the next century, for an emissions scenario close to IPCC 'business as usual'. Inclusion of the cooling effects of sulphate aerosols is expected to reduce this to about 2.5°C.
- By the 2050s, tropical grasslands and forests will be at risk of decline, whereas many temperate and boreal forests may continue to expand in response to climate change and increasing atmospheric CO_2.
- The current ability of vegetation to absorb 20-30% of human-made CO_2 emissions will be maintained initially, but may fall away to zero during the second half of the next century as a result of a decline in tropical vegetation. Consequently, a larger fraction of CO_2 emitted by human activities would remain in the atmosphere thereafter.
- Climate change is likely to exacerbate the pressure put on water resources by an increasing global population, particularly in Africa, Central America, the Indian sub-continent and southern Europe. By the 2050s, the models indicate that there could be about a further 100 million people living in countries with extreme water stress due to climate change alone.
- Global food supply is expected to meet the overall needs of a growing world population but significant regional variations in crop yields due to climate change could lead to increased risk of hunger for an additional 50 million people by the 2080s in the tropics, particularly in Africa.
- Without measures adopted specifically to tackle rising sea levels, increased flooding is calculated to affect some 200 million people worldwide by the 2080s. Around 25% of the world's coastal wetlands could be lost by this time due to sea-level rise alone.

Overall, the results suggest that climate change is likely to intensify the already increasing pressures on various sectors. Although the impact of climate change may, in some cases, be smaller than other stresses on the environment, even relatively small changes can have serious adverse effects, especially where there may be critical thresholds, where development is already marginal, or where a region is less able to implement adaptation measures.

Global assessments can mask important regional differences, and regional impacts have been evaluated here wherever possible. Although some sectors in some regions may experience beneficial effects as a result of climate change, other regions and sectors are likely to face adverse changes. Regions particularly at risk from combined detrimental effects across several sectors are often those least able to adapt.

By taking a partially integrated look at how several key sectors will be affected by future climate change, this study has helped quantify some major impacts both on a global and, to a lesser extent, regional scale. It represents a step towards improving the scientific understanding of the impacts of climate change, and highlights both the complex nature of the problem and the urgent need for further research in this area.

- The above is an extract from *Climate change and its impacts – a global perspective*, produced by the Met. Office. See page 41 for address details.

© *The Met. Office*
December, 1997

FOR THE NEXT 100 YEARS

WEATHER FORECAST

Ken Pyne

Climate change

Scientific certainties and uncertainties

Climate change is perhaps the most pressing and urgent environmental issue on the world's agenda. In 1995 the UN Intergovernmental Panel on Climate Change (IPCC) concluded that 'the balance of evidence suggests a discernible human influence on global climate'.

The earth's systems of air, water and land have always been dynamic. Studies of ancient climates show that there have been alternating periods of global warmth and global chill at various times. Sometimes the transitions from one state to another have been abrupt, at other times the rate of change has been slow, but in all cases change has been driven by natural processes.

But now evidence is gathering that human activities are changing or perhaps accelerating climate change. The earth appears to be warming. Can we distinguish human effects on climate change from the background of natural change? More importantly, can we predict the rate and extent of future changes and their impacts on our lives?

Here we spell out what we know as facts about climate change and what can be predicted from those facts. We also want to make clear where there are uncertainties in both our knowledge and our predictions.

Widely accepted facts
- Average global temperature has risen by 0.6°C in the last 130 years.
- Carbon dioxide levels in the atmosphere have risen by about 25% in the last 20 years, increasing from about 280 parts per million to 356 parts per million today.
- Methane levels in the atmosphere have doubled over the last 100 years.

- Nitrous oxide levels are rising at about 0.25% each year.
- Carbon dioxide, methane and nitrous oxide are all greenhouse gases which trap radiation emitted from the earth's surface, keeping the earth warmer than it otherwise would be.
- Carbon dioxide, methane and nitrous oxide levels are rising mainly as a result of human activities connected with energy generation, transport and agriculture.
- The order of importance in contributing to human-induced global warming is carbon dioxide (70%), methane (20%), nitrous oxide plus other gases (10%).
- Temperature has not increased as much as you would expect from the observed carbon dioxide increase. It is thought that tiny particles in the atmosphere from, for instance, industrial activities or volcanic eruptions, reflect sunlight and produce a cooling effect.

- A doubling of carbon dioxide levels would theoretically lead to an average global temperature rise of 1-2°C if all other factors remained the same. But in reality other factors will also change in response to rising temperature and many produce feedbacks, some negative, some positive. For example, water vapour in the atmosphere increases as temperature rises and is itself a potent greenhouse gas.

What is likely to happen?
Global consequences
- If greenhouse gas emissions continue on a 'business as usual' basis, models predict that carbon dioxide levels will double from pre-industrial levels by the end of the next century. When the effect of other factors such as increased water vapour is added, the estimated average global temperature rise will be between 1.5 and 4.5°C, the most likely value being 2.5°C.

- The rise in temperature will produce an impact on a wide range of climate-related factors.
- Global sea levels are likely to rise by about 50cm over the next century, and will continue to rise further in the future. Low-lying coasts will flood and some habitats such as saltmarshes will be lost unless they can be protected from flooding.
- We might expect more extreme weather events – heatwaves, floods, droughts, storms – but it is impossible to predict where these are likely to occur with the present generation of models.
- The world's vegetation zones will undergo major changes, in particular boundary shifts between grasslands, forests and shrublands.
- Deserts will become hotter, desertification will extend and is more likely to become irreversible.
- Half the world's glaciers could melt and Arctic ice would be reduced in extent. When ice melts, the amount of solar radiation which can be absorbed by the exposed land increases so warming will be amplified further.
- Freshwater systems will experience changes in temper-ature, flows and levels, affecting bio-diversity, water supplies and probably water quality. Human conflict over access to water resources may increase.
- Agricultural productivity is likely to vary across regions. Although global productivity may stay about the same, there may be increased risk of famine in arid and semi-arid regions.
- Mass movements of people away from flooded or arid regions would cause conflicts and health problems.
- Human and animal diseases may spread to new areas.

UK consequences
The UK will be directly or indirectly affected by most of the expected global impacts of climate change. The specific effects will depend upon regional changes which are impossible to predict accurately at present. A general northwards shift by 50–80 km per decade of natural

habitats and agricultural zones is likely. Forestry and some forms of farming are likely to benefit, but significant impacts are likely on soils, wildlife, water resources and agri-culture in the south.

Uncertainties

Most scientists agree that the climate is warming as the result of human activities, but uncertainties abound at almost all the stages of climate prediction. Some of these un-certainties are sufficient to lead a very few experts to doubt that warming is happening at all. Other experts query the extent to which the observed warming is unusual or how much of it can be attributed to human activities. Much of the current research effort is aimed at reducing the uncertainties.

Uncertainties over the facts
Carbon budgets – carbon moves between the atmosphere, where it occurs mainly as carbon dioxide, and all other parts of the environment – soil, vegetation, oceans, rocks and so on – forming the global carbon budget. We are not sure what determines how much carbon is in which part of the earth's systems and the rate at which it moves between the parts.

Temperatures fluctuate annu-ally and over much longer timescales associated with the natural variability of the climate. Accurate records using instruments have only been made for about a century. Past records are inferred from other evidence. Identifying small warming trends against this background variation is difficult.

Solar radiation varies due to physical changes in the sun, the best known being the 11-year sun-spot cycle. Variations detected using satellites over the last 20 years are

small, less than 1%. It is not clear whether variations over a long timescale might be more significant and what effect any of this variation has on the warming of the earth.

Uncertainties over climate 'feedbacks'
Once climate change begins, many other factors we have been measuring or estimating also start to change. Some can increase the rate of change, others can produce feedbacks which slow things down. Some examples are:
- Clouds: clouds can reflect incoming solar radiation back into space, keeping heat out. But clouds can also prevent radiation from the earth's surface escaping, thus keeping heat in. So the effects can be positive or negative depending on the height, temper-ature and reflecting properties of the clouds, all of which vary in time and from place to place. The effects of clouds are poorly under-stood and they remain one of the biggest uncertainties.
- Water vapour: a warmer atmo-sphere can hold more water vapour which is a powerful greenhouse gas, thus amplifying the warming by positive feedback.
- Plant growth may increase if carbon dioxide rises, thus absorb-ing more carbon from the atmos-phere – a negative feedback.
- Polar ice sheets will melt to some extent as temperatures rise, but melting will be partially balanced by greater snowfall over polar areas. Arctic ice sheets will melt faster than snow will accumulate, therefore adding to sea level rises. But in the Antarctic, recent studies suggest that the inter-actions of ice shelves (the parts of the Antarctic Ice Sheet which extend out over the ocean) with the waters beneath are complex, and that warmer temperatures will not necessarily result in thinner ice sheets and shelves in the southern hemisphere.
- Reflectance – changes in the distribution of vegetation in warmer climates may alter the reflectance and thus the capacity of the earth to absorb heat. Less snow cover over the continents

of the northern hemisphere in warmer conditions will mean more solar radiation absorbed by the darker surface.

Uncertainties over 'flipping systems'

Few of the systems in climate models are simple, as many of the factors listed above indicate. Doubled input does not necessarily lead to doubled output. One particular feature of complex systems is that under particular conditions, they may change abruptly and massively. Small incremental changes in one variable, such as the amount of a greenhouse gas, could trigger a switch response to a different state in one of the earth's systems.

One example may be 'El Niño', a periodic event in the Pacific Ocean in which sea temperatures rise sharply on the eastern side and have a strong influence on the weather patterns throughout the world. It is not certain what sets off this sudden but quite natural change in ocean currents and movements of air. We also do not know how such events may change in a warmer world.

Another example may be the North Atlantic circulation system known as 'The Atlantic Conveyor Belt'. This is a current system which carries warm surface water northwards and returns cold deep water to the south. It results in a transfer of free heat to the atmosphere equivalent to 30,000 times the power-generating capacity of the UK. This gives western Europe its present temperate climate. Disruptions to the system in the past have coincided with rapid transitions into and out of ice ages. Models show that disruptions could occur if more fresh water enters the Arctic Ocean as a result of global warming.

Can we change the course of climate change?

Carbon dioxide has an effective lifetime in the atmosphere of about 100 years, so concentrations respond very slowly to changes in emissions. If we stabilise carbon dioxide emissions (as agreed by developed countries at the 1992 Summit in Rio de Janeiro) the rate of climate change will slow down. But we would need to reduce current carbon dioxide emissions by about 60% globally to prevent carbon dioxide concentrations from rising further.

• The above is an extract from *Climate change – Scientific certainties and uncertainties*, produced by the Natural Environment Research Council. See page 41 for address details.

© Natural Environment Research Council

The problem in a nutshell

Human activities are increasing the concentrations of naturally-occurring 'greenhouse gases' in the atmosphere. These gases, which include carbon dioxide (CO_2) and methane, trap solar heat in the atmosphere, so warming the surface of the planet. The IPCC forecasts that, under reasonable assumptions about future human activities – its mid-range 'business as usual scenario' – concentrations of greenhouse gases will rise sufficiently over the next century to cause a world-wide average temperature rise of between 1.5°C and 4°C.

The cooling effect of other pollution, through shading the planet's surface, may reduce this to perhaps 1°C-3.5°C, says the IPCC. But this would still be enough to trigger major changes in local climates and ecosystems and disruption of many human activities, including causing famine and widespread flooding of inhabited areas. Global mean surface temperatures have already increased by between 0.3°C and 0.6°C, probably as a result of human activity.

The main human source of greenhouse gases is the burning of fossil fuels, such as coal, oil and gas, which releases CO_2. Other sources include deforestation, which also releases CO_2, and agriculture, which through a variety of routes releases methane and other gases such as nitrous oxide. Carbon dioxide, the main man-made greenhouse gas, has a lifetime in the atmosphere of a century or more.

The main human source of greenhouse gases is the burning of fossil fuels, such as coal, oil and gas, which releases CO_2

Even if global carbon dioxide emissions were to be stabilised near their current levels, concentrations would increase throughout the 21st century and would continue to increase slowly for several hundred years afterwards. Because of this, substantial cuts in emissions will be necessary to stabilise concentrations in the atmosphere.

As the world's climate begins to change, the planet will respond, sometimes in ways that will accelerate warming, sometimes in ways that will slow it down. Critical factors include the response to warming of clouds, forests, ice cover and ocean circulation. The overall effect of these 'feedbacks' remains uncertain. Scientists are not yet certain how sensitive the climate is to the direct 'radiative forcing' of increased greenhouse gases. This gap in knowledge explains the large margins of error surrounding current predictions of climate change. But there is a consensus that there will be significant warming.

• The above is an extract from *Explaining climate change*, produced by WWF. See page 41 for address details.
© WWF

The issue of winners and losers

Climate change scenarios

Geographical location will influence how individual countries are affected by climate change. Scientists find it difficult to forecast the regional impacts of climate change. However, their global forecast of rising sea-levels, atmospheric warming, and weather instability suggest that countries with coastal and eco-logically-fragile regions will be the biggest 'losers'. Countries located at higher latitudes, on the other hand, may actually be climate change 'winners', at least in the short term.

The impact on agricultural productivity will vary from country to country. In general, warmer weather should increase both growing seasons and crop growth rates, except in areas that are already extremely hot. However, agriculture also depends on the quantity of rainfall, its distribution throughout the year, and the amount of moisture remaining in the soil. In many arid and semi-arid regions, rainfall may decline, devastating agriculture. It is difficult to predict which agricultural zones will be advantaged or dis-advantaged by climate change. One study[1] concludes that Canada, the US, and Southern Europe might experience a decrease in agricultural production, whereas Russia, Northern Europe, and Japan might increase their agricultural output.

Countries with large coastal areas less than one metre above the current sea-level are expected to be big losers. These countries include small island states, archipelagos, and coral atoll nations, such as the Maldives, the Marshall Islands, and Tuvalu. While the Netherlands has already made an enormous invest-ment in protecting its coastline, poorer coastal countries, such as Bangladesh will find coastal protection hard to afford.

Countries located partly or entirely in ecologically fragile regions are also at high risk. These regions include arctic and sub-arctic, desert and semi-desert, and high-mountain ecosystems. Their response to climate change would depend in good part on the rate of change. If the climate changes too rapidly, many plant, animal, and insect species will be unable to migrate or adapt. As species die off, these regions would become more prone to soil erosion and other damage, particularly if climate change also results in more frequent storms.

Poor countries may be the biggest losers of all. If climate change has its predicted impacts, many developing countries may lack the necessary resources for protecting themselves. 'Richer is safer because wealth provides the capacity for flexible responses to unwanted risks, especially when precise under-standing of [these risks] is not available or perhaps not even possible . . . as is the case with global climate change'.[2] In addition to all its other negative effects, then, climate change may also widen the gap between rich and poor.

If climate change begins to take a heavy toll, countries may perceive each other as relative winners and losers. Clearly, climate change is not in the long-term interests of any country. However, perceived differences in the global distribution of short-term negative impacts would have powerful political implications. So too would an awareness that some countries are more responsible for greenhouse gas emissions than are others. Accusations and conflict could be expected to increase.

Is it counterproductive to raise the issue of winners and losers? By identifying countries as winners and losers, we may undermine the unity needed for concerted action against climate change. Says US Vice

President Al Gore, 'The fact is that the change is so radical and so rapid that it disrupts the society and the political structure. I just think that it is a mistake to put it in terms of winners and losers. I think that the earth is a loser.'[3] On the other hand, there may also be a risk in not making the distinction between winners and losers. Suggests one climate change expert, 'Pro-ponents for action on global warming profess that there are no winners, while everyone agrees with them in public but believes the opposite. This could sharply reduce the credibility of the proponents.'[4]

References

1 M. Parry, et al., eds., *The Impact* of *Climate Variations on Agriculture*, Laxenburg International Institute for Applied Systems Analysis (1989).

2 W. Fulkerson, et al., International *Impacts of Global Climate Change*, Testimony to US House Appropriations Subcommittee on Foreign Operations,

3 S. Schneider, *Global Warming: Are We Entering the Greenhouse Century?*, San Francisco Sierra Club Books (1989).

4 M. Glantz, *Assessing the Impacts of Climate: The Issue of Winners and Losers in a Global Climate Change Context*, paper prepared for conference on The Adaptive Responses to Sea Level Rise and Other Impacts of Global Climate Change, Miami, November 27 – December 1, 1989.

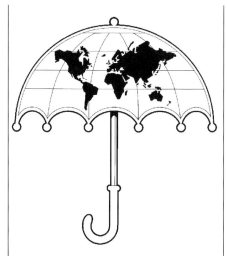

1997 — a year of weather extremes

Climate change is not just about global warming. Climate scientists predict it will mean more droughts, torrential rain, floods, hurricanes and heatwaves. This is a selection of some of the worst weather events of 1997. Similar events have occured with an increasing frequency and intensity over recent decades.

North Dakota (US), Southern Manitoba (Canada)
April/May – worst flooding of Red River in 100 years due to record late spring snowfalls – 60,000 people evacuated, economic losses more than US $1 billion.

Southern Spain and Southern Portugal
November – flash floods due to torrential rain, at least 31 people killed, 10% of cotton crop lost in Andalucia

Czech Republic, Poland, East Germany
July/August – one-a-century floods due to unusually heavy periods of rainfall: 120 people dead, 187,000 people evacuated, costs estimated at least, costs estimated at least $5 billion

China (North)
Worst drought this century; more than 50% of wheat crop damaged

South and South-East China
June: torrential rain, more than 1 million people homeless, 90,000 tonnes of grain destroyed, economic losses $1,25 billion.

Western US (California, Nevada, Oregon, Idaho)
January – torrential rains, flash floods, river flooding, 125,000 people evacuated, economic losses US $42 billion, more than 100 km² of farmland destroyed

Papua New Guinea
Unprecedented drought, crop failure, 150,000 people on brink of starvation, 1/2 million undernourished

East Africa (Somalia, Ethiopia, Kenya)
November: worst floods within living memory – 800,000 people homeless, at least115 people dead.

Mexico – Western states of Guerrero & Oaxaca incl. Acapulco
October: Hurricane Pauline – 400 people dead, 300,000 people homeless, 97% of corn crop destroyed, 60% of hotels damaged in Acapulco

East Africa (Somalia, Ethiopia, Kenya)
Summer: failure of rains, crop failures, food shortage for at least 5.5 million people

Australia
Driest 13-month period on record in Melbourne area; severe droughts in much of Eastern and South-Eastern Australia

Bangladesh
July: torrential rain (200mm in 24 hours), landslides, 1,200 km2 of farmland flooded/damaged, 100,000 people evacuated, 104 deaths, economic losses US $230 million.

Indonesia, Malaysia, Borneo
Worst drought for decades, monsoon delayed, forest fires raging on 1 million ha, resulting in dangerous smog levels in many cities; cocoa and other cash crops damaged

Source: Friends of the Earth

The very model of a global argument

After listening to all the arguments of both sides in the global warming debate, one cannot avoid the conclusion that nobody can really be sure about the state of the earth's health. By William Hartston

Let's sort out this global warming thing, shall we? It's perfectly simple: when we burn fossil fuels, it expels carbon dioxide into the atmosphere. And carbon dioxide is one of the greenhouse gases which prevent heat escaping. So the more carbon dioxide is up there, the hotter we become.

That's all very well, but doesn't the carbon dioxide also stop the sun's rays reaching us, thereby cooling us down?
That's what we thought 25 years ago when we worried about an impending ice age. But now we know that the greenhouse heating-up effect is greater than the so-called volcano effect that cools us.

How do we know that?
We've been monitoring the CO_2 levels in the atmosphere and there's not much doubt that they correlate with rising temperature.

You mean that the temperature's been going up and the CO_2 has been rising, and you suspect a causal connection.
It's far more than that. The claim that we're at the end of a small ice age, and the earth's warming up anyway, and CO_2 emissions have nothing to do with it, simply cannot be sustained – the correlations between temperature and gas emissions are too precise for that. Anyway, our computer models of the behaviour of the atmosphere offer an excellent simulation of what has been going on.

Do the predictions of global catastrophe come from the same computer models?
They sure do.

But to predict catastrophe, you must be extrapolating way beyond the range for which the computer models have been verified.
Look, if – to simplify the matter – you have a linear correlation between two quantities between a given range, then by the laws of physics you can expect it to continue linearly for some way beyond that range.

But it's not linear, is it?
No. I was just giving an example to simplify it.

What about Mount Pinatubo? Didn't I read that its eruption caused a drop in world temperature of about 0.2 °C, which is equivalent to most of the man-made global warming over the past century?
So what?

Well, what if global warming led to more volcanic eruptions which could more than cancel out the bad effects?
That's pure speculation. We don't know enough about volcanoes to be able to say anything of the sort.

And what about the algae that consume atmospheric CO_2 and sink it to the bottom of the sea. Isn't there some evidence that they are becoming more numerous and helping maintain a balance?
Tricky chaps, algae. We don't know much about them either.

So neither algae nor volcanoes feature in your mathematical models?
Some models have attempted to incorporate them, but they are unreliable. When our current models do the job so well, why make them more complex?

Personally, I'm rather enjoying the milder weather we've been having.
Now you're just being silly. This interview is concluded.

© The Independent
December, 1997

Potential effects of climate change in the UK

This information summarises the work of the Climate Change Impacts Review Group (CCIRG) which was set up at the request of the Department of the Environment to consider the potential impacts of climate change in the UK [1]. The CCIRG is made up of representatives from academia, industry and commerce, and constitutes a panel of experts able to discuss the potential effects of climate change in the UK.

The impacts discussed in this article are not predictions but possible outcomes suggested by climate models [2,3,4]. It is by no means certain that climate change will have the following impacts. However, the scientific consensus suggests that changes may occur as described, but the rate and extent of the impacts are uncertain.

Climate change in UK

Climate change has potential risks for the UK. Most critical of these risks is the frequency and changes in extreme climatic conditions such as hot spells, drought and storms. It is likely that the occurrence of hot, dry summers will increase, while the chance of extreme cold winters will decrease. At this stage in the scientific understanding of the effects of climate change it is impossible to speculate on the effect of climate change for other extremes such as the occurrence of storms.

Climate change will have potential effects on hydrology; impacts to water resources, water quality, evapotranspiration and soil moisture would have serious implications for the environment, and the industrial, commercial and transport sectors in the UK.

Soils, flora, fauna and associated ecosystems are generally very sensitive to variations in moisture. There could be potentially large changes in landscape and habitat with some species being favoured to the detriment of others. Particular attention must be focused on the proper management of natural and semi-natural ecosystems. Agriculture, horticulture, forestry and the water industry will be particularly sensitive to variations in rainfall and the various hydrological processes but adaptation to conditions will be possible.

Coastal zones are an area of potential risk which deserve special attention in the UK. There is a possibility that changes in the climate and sea level will effect coastal and estuarine zones. These areas contain a large proportion of the UK population, manufacturing industry, energy production facilities, valued natural environments (beaches and wetlands), recreational amenities and mineral extraction sites. Existing problems such as coastal erosion, storm surge damage, degradation of wetlands and estuaries, and groundwater contamination could be exacerbated by climate change.

Specific effects of climate change in the UK

The potential effects of climate change in the UK are examined under the following headings: soils; flora/fauna and landscape; agriculture, horticulture and forestry; coastal regions; water resources; energy; minerals extraction; manufacturing; construction; transport; the financial sector; and recreation and tourism.

Soils

Higher temperatures which may result from climate change would mean that the water-holding capacity of soils is likely to decrease and soil moisture deficits increase. These changes would have a major effect on the types of crops, trees or other vegetation that the soils in a particular area can support, and by extension, the whole pattern of land use in the UK. Changes in soil moisture content would have wide-ranging effects on cultivation, sowing and other practices associated with crop production.

The stability of building foundations and other structures especially in central, eastern and southern England, where clay soils with large shrink-swell potential are abundant, would be affected if summers became drier and winters wetter.

Loss of organic matter in soils would increase significantly under conditions of drier summers and wetter winters. The loss of organic matter would affect the stability of soil structure, ecological habitats nationally and agricultural use in southern England. Currently poorly drained mineral soils could become drier and hence less of a problem, whereas, close to low-lying coastal area, well-drained soils could become poorly drained.

If the water table rose with the rising sea level, a change in soil processes would result. Existing land drainage schemes could become ineffective and new drainage schemes would be needed if land were to remain suitable for arable cropping. Soils affected by rising sea levels would become saline and unsuitable for the growing of crops. The vulnerability of subsoil components of engineering structures to corrosion would increase.

Flora, fauna & landscape

Any sustained rise in mean surface temperature exceeding 1°C, with the associated extreme weather events and soil water deficits, would have marked effects on the UK flora and fauna. If such conditions occur there may be significant movements of species northwards and to higher elevations; species which do not extend their ranges will not necessarily be affected adversely as many species have the capacity to adapt to climatic change. However, predicted rates of climate change may be too great for many species (e.g. most trees) to adapt genetically. Many native species and communities would be adversely affected and may be lost to the UK, especially endangered species which occur in isolated damp, coastal or cool habitats. It is likely that there would be an increased invasion and spread of alien weeds, pests, diseases and viruses, some of which may be potentially harmful. Increased numbers of foreign species of invertebrates, birds and mammals may out-compete native species.

Agriculture, horticulture & forestry

Climate changes are likely to have a substantial effect on plant growth, and by extension plant productivity. In general, higher temperatures would decrease the yields of cereal crops (such as wheat) although the yield of crops such as potatoes, sugar beet and forest trees would tend to increase. However, pests such as the Colorado beetle on potatoes and rhizomania on sugar beet, currently thought to be limited by temperature, could become more prevalent in the future. The length of the

growing season for grasses and trees would increase by about 15 days per °C increase in mean surface temperature, an increase that could improve the viability of grassland, animal production and forestry in the uplands.

If temperatures increase, there would be opportunities to introduce new tree species and crops that are currently grown in warmer climes. Maize and sunflower crops might be grown for their seed/grain yield and for animal fodder over much of the arable area of the UK if temperatures rose by about 1 to 1.5°C from present values.

Coastal regions

Increases in mean sea level would lead to an increased frequency of higher sea levels and coastal flooding. If there were also increases in the frequency and magnitude of storms, storm surges and waves would further increase the likelihood of flooding.

A number of low-lying areas are particularly vulnerable to sea level rise: these include the coasts of East Anglia, Lancashire and the Yorkshire/Lincolnshire area, the Essex mudflats, the Sussex coastal towns, the Thames estuary, parts of the north Wales coast, the Clyde/Forth estuaries and Belfast Lough. Flooding would result in damage to structures and short-term disruption to transport, manufacturing and the domestic sector. In addition, longer term damage to agricultural land, engineering structures such as buildings and coastal power stations, rail and road systems, would occur in some areas due to salt infiltration.

The success of adaptive responses to changes in the frequency of coastal flooding will depend on the rate at which these changes occur.

Groundwater provides about 30% of the water supply in the UK.

A rise in the water table associated with higher sea levels may increase the salination of groundwater over long periods, with consequent effects on agriculture and water supply.

Water resources

Water resources would generally benefit from wetter winters, but warmer summers with longer growing seasons and increased evaporation would lead to greater pressures on water resources, especially in the south-east of the UK. Increased rainfall variability, even in a slightly wetter climate, could lead to more droughts in any region in the UK. Higher temperatures would lead to increased demand for water and higher peak demands, requiring increased investment in water resources and infrastructure. An increase in temperature would increase demand for irrigation and abstraction from agriculture would compete with abstractions and for piped water supply by other users.

Many activities use a large amount of water in production; these industries could be severely curtailed as a result of drought. Many existing power stations also rely on river water for cooling, and climate change may result in a reduction in the availability of cooling water, particularly during the summer months.

Energy

Higher temperatures would have a pronounced effect on energy demand. Space heating needs would decrease substantially but increased demand for air conditioning may entail greater electricity use. Total energy demand is, however, likely to fall as a result of climate change. Of great importance is the fact that all petroleum refineries and half of the present UK power station capacity are located in coastal or estuarine regions. The vulnerability of coastal or estuarine areas to storm surges resulting from sea-level rise means sea defences may need to be strengthened in order to protect against flooding.

Mineral extraction

Projected changes in temperature and rainfall are unlikely to result in significant technical problems for the coal, industrial minerals and aggregates industries in the UK. However, rises in sea and estuary levels and changes in the water table and salinity would, in some areas, be detrimental to land-based mineral extraction and dredging. There could be increases in pumping and mineral processing costs, and the restoration of extraction sites would be more complicated.

Manufacturing
Manufacturing industry contributes approximately 30% of the UK's gross domestic product and accounts for over 35% of the UK's income from exports. It is, therefore, an important sector to consider in relation to the impacts of climate change. Most manufacturing industries should be capable of adapting to climate change but the major concern for this sector, 40% of which is located in coastal and estuarine areas, relates to the potential for sea level rise. Increase in temperature, with a reduction in severe winter frosts, would be likely to improve productivity in some areas such as the building industry, to improve the transport of raw materials and finished products, and to decrease disruptions in production due to weather. Repeated annual droughts could adversely affect certain manufacturing industries requiring large amounts of processed water, such as paper making, brewing, food industries and power generation and chemical industries.

Construction
Although warmer winters would confer some benefits for construction productivity, increased winter rainfall would adversely affect building operations. However, the greatest negative impacts on construction are likely to arise from the combination of sea-level rise and alterations in inland water hydrology. Design risk codes, currently based on historical climate records, will need to alter accordingly.

Transport
Sensitivity to weather and climate change is high for all forms of transport. Snow and ice present a very difficult weather-related problem for the transport sector. A reduction in the frequency, severity and duration of winter freeze would

be likely under conditions associated with climate change and could be beneficial. However, any increase in the frequency of severe gale episodes could increase disruption to all transport sectors.

Financial sector
Little information exists on the potential impacts of climate change upon the various activities within the financial sector, except for the insurance industry, which would be immediately affected by a shift in the risk of damaging weather events arising from climate change. If the risk of flooding increased due to sea-level rise, this would expose the financial sector to the greatest potential losses (the value of the property protected by the Thames Barrier is estimated to be in the region of £10 to £20 billion).

If climate change and sea-level rise affect socio-economic activities, the appraisal of existing and new investment opportunities would also be affected, particularly in agriculture and for coastal regions. The role of insurance in protecting the most vulnerable areas or activities would also change.

Recreation & tourism
UK tourism has an international dimension which is sensitive to any change in climate altering the competitive balance of holiday destinations world-wide. If any changes to warmer, drier summer conditions occur, this could stimulate an overall increase in tourism in the UK. However, any significant increase in rainfall, windspeed or cloud cover could offset some of the general advantages expected from higher temperatures.

References
[1] Department of the Environment, 1991. *The Potential Effects of Climate Change in the United Kingdom.* HMSO
[2] Houghton, J.T., Meira Filho, L.G., Bruce, J., Lee, H., Callander, B.A., Haites, E., Harris, N. & Maskell, K. (eds.). *Climate Change 1994: Radiative Forcing of Climate Change, and An Evaluation of the IPCC IS92 Emission Scenarios,* Intergovernmental Panel on Climate Change, Cambridge University Press, Cambridge, 1995.
[3] Houghton, J.T., Jenkins, G.J. & Ephraums, J.J. (eds.). *Climate Change: The IPCC Scientific Assessment,* Intergovernmental Panel on Climate Change, Cambridge University Press, Cambridge, 1990.
[4] Houghton, J.T., Callander, B.A. & Varney, S.K. (eds.). *Climate Change 1992: The supplementary report to the IPCC Scientific Assessment,* Intergovernmental Panel on Climate Change, Cambridge University Press, Cambridge, 1992.

© *Global Climate Change Information Programme*

Warmer weather brings threat of malaria and cholera

Global warming could bring olive trees to southern Britain as the world's climate changes more rapidly in the next 100 years than in the previous 10,000

But the rise in temperature could also lead to outbreaks of tropical diseases such as cholera and malaria. Jeremy Laurance, Health Editor, anticipates the hidden dangers of warmer days.

Rising temperatures across the world will spread tropical illnesses to Europe and North America and change the global pattern of disease, scientists predict.

Malaria, cholera, tick-borne fevers and respiratory illnesses are all expected to grow as a result of the accumulation of carbon dioxide, methane and other gases in the atmosphere which is believed to be causing global warming.

While warmer temperatures may be welcomed by wine producers and olive growers hoping to extend their operations to northern Europe, the spread of diseases could bring misery to many.

Specialists at the London School of Hygiene and Tropical Medicine and the Royal Free Hospital School of Medicine have estimated the likely health effects of the 1–3.5 degrees centigrade rise in global temperatures forecast by the Intergovernmental Panel on Climate Change, a United Nations scientific body set up to advise governments world-wide.

Writing in the *British Medical Journal*, Professors Tony McMichael and Andrew Haines say storms, floods and heatwaves are likely to increase. Air pollution is likely to worsen, especially summer smogs which are sensitive to a variation in temperatures.

> **Rising temperatures across the world will spread tropical illnesses to Europe and North America**

Diseases likely to become more common in Europe include malaria, which was widespread in Britain until improved public health measures eliminated it in the early part of this century. Viral encephalitis, a swelling of the brain spread by ticks, and Lyme disease, also spread by ticks and causing arthritis and skin rashes, are expected to grow. Leishmaniasis, a disease affecting the liver and causing fever and death if untreated, which is found in the eastern Mediterranean, is also predicted to spread northwards. It is carried by the sandfly.

Professor McMichael said yesterday that cases of local transmission of malaria in New York and Europe had increased in the last decade. 'It is difficult to say whether the malarial mosquito will come over the horizon in Britain. What we can say is that climate change will make it easier for this disease to spread.'

Cholera broke out in Peru, South America, in 1991 for the first time for 100 years. US scientists believe warming of the coastal waters and increased dumping of phosphate and nitrate wastes stimulated the growth of algae which acted as a natural host for the cholera bacteria.

Professor McMichael said the same algae were common in the Mediterranean. 'If there were sufficient shifts in the temperature of coastal waters in Britain it could be a problem here too,' he said. Individuals and society had to tackle the problem of global warming by reducing production of carbon dioxide, he warned.

© The Independent
September, 1997

HE WENT TO BRITAIN AND DRANK THE WATER

THE LAGOS HOSPITAL

YEAR 2098

KenPyne

Long range weather forecast: hot, dry and French

In 30 years the climate of Europe will have moved 150 miles north.
By Paul Brown, Environment Correspondent

Southern England will have the climate of the Champagne region of France in 25 years' time and Yorkshire will replace Kent as the Garden of England, the Environment Secretary, John Gummer, said yesterday.

Launching his department's review of the effects of climate change on the UK, he said the climate was already noticeably changing and would continue to do so until the 'familiar landscape of the Cotswolds and Suffolk will be growing sunflowers and maize' by 2025.

After another 25 years, the climate will have shifted again, with southern England resembling the Bordeaux region and the Champagne climate moving to Yorkshire.

The report predicts that the south and east of England will become much drier as well as warmer, with summer water shortages becoming normal, while the north-west will become far wetter. Trees would suffer in the south but forests would grow 25 per cent faster in the north and in Scotland.

Mr Gummer said that while the predictions brought some good news – for example a boost to tourism – on balance it was bad, particularly for counties in southern England.

In 30 years, the climate of Europe will have moved 150 miles north. For example, the hot dry conditions in Spain will move to France. Paris will have the climate of the south of France and Spain will be mostly desert.

It means southern England will enjoy the same climate as the Loire valley and therefore the whole pattern of agriculture in Europe would have to change. There would be enormous need to adapt quickly and it remained to be seen whether Europe would still be able to feed itself.

Rain and windstorms will become more frequent in Britain and do more damage than at present. A rise in the sea level of up to one foot (35cm) on the east coast will threaten low-lying areas.

> **The hot dry conditions in Spain will move to France. Paris will have the climate of the south of France and Spain will be mostly desert**

The UK has already authorised an increase in the height of sea walls but storm surges caused by the combination of high tide and wind will threaten East Anglia, the Humber region, Teesside and the Firth of Forth. On the west coast, Avonmouth, Morecambe Bay and northern Cumbria have coastal lowlands which could be affected.

Some plant and animal species will die out, others will have to migrate northwards. Insects like the malaria-carrying mosquito will be able to thrive in southern Britain.

The report was launched two weeks before Mr Gummer goes to Geneva for talks on the UN Convention on Climate Change. Britain and Europe are expected to spearhead moves to cut carbon dioxide emissions to try to slow down the process of global warming, so that the world has a chance to adapt to the changes.

As a first step, Britain is proposing to reduce carbon dioxide emissions to 5 to 10 per cent below 1990 levels by 2010.

Mr Gummer emphasised that it was too late to stop the climate changing because of the pollution already in the atmosphere.

© *The Guardian*
July, 1996

An iceberg on tap

Drought busters may be towed from Arctic. By David Derbyshire, Science Correspondent

Global climate changes over the next century are likely to have a dramatic effect on human health, an expert warned yesterday.

They could lead to altered patterns of diseases such as malaria, malnutrition because of the impact on agriculture and impaired development in vulnerable populations.

A warning came from Professor Anthony McMichael of the London School of Hygiene and Tropical Medicine, in a report published in the *British Medical Journal*.

Giant icebergs a mile long may be towed down the North Sea from above the Arctic Circle to supply water to drought-hit Britain.

With underground reservoirs and rivers at record low levels after three years of poor rainfall – and the current dry spell doing little to alleviate the situation – the astonishing plan is being considered.

The Essex and Suffolk Water company has discussed the feasibility of the project with its counterparts in Norway.

'It does sound a little fanciful, but we have a duty to investigate all sources of supply,' said customer service manager Brian Olley. 'Getting an iceberg across the sea would be a bit of a challenge. It would probably be rather expensive, because we would have to build plants on the coast to convert the ice back into water and then treat it.'

The average family uses 45,000 gallons of water a year. An iceberg one mile long, 1,000ft wide and 900ft deep contains around 20billion gallons, enough to supply 445,000 families for one year.

Experts say a handful of tugs should be powerful enough to shift one of the colossal frozen chunks, although the voyage would take several weeks. The iceberg would

shrink during the journey, but there would still be plenty of it left by the time it arrived in British waters. However, that is when real problems would probably begin.

To melt the iceberg, engineers would have to drill into its side, warming it, then pump the semi-frozen slush ashore. Or they could break it into smaller segments, float them to the dockside, load them on lorries and melt them into reservoirs.

But almost all reservoirs are miles inland and the pipe network has been designed to move water towards the coast. That means a seaside reservoir, processing plant and pipe network would have to be built – or the meltwater would have to be pumped to the nearest reservoir.

A more serious option is to tow an iceberg up a river or specially-built canal connected to a reservoir. A sluice gate would then channel the slowly melting water into the reservoir.

To speed up melting, the frozen mass could be covered with a dark

material to absorb the heat. Essex and Suffolk Water needs 100million gallons a day for its 1.4million customers and already pipes in half its supplies from neighbouring companies.

Previously, water companies have flirted with the idea of transporting water from Scotland on barges or storing giant bags of fresh water off the coast.

A spokesman for the Water Companies Association admitted that turning icebergs into tapwater would be costly and difficult. 'But companies have to explore the options because at the moment resources are at historic lows, partly because of the increase in demand and partly because of the weather.'

True icebergs are made from fresh water. They are formed when glaciers flow to the coast, dropping vast chunks into the sea. Most come from the fjord glaciers of Greenland and the shelf ice of Antarctica.

Only one-fifth of an iceberg is visible above water. Some can be 2,400ft deep – three times as high as Britain's tallest building, Canary Wharf. Few rise more than 200ft above water.

Plans to use icebergs for drinking water have been around since the Second World War. At one time the Saudis planned to ship them to the Middle East.

Some icebergs have survived intact for 3,000 years. The most famous was the one struck by the luxury liner Titanic in 1912, with the loss of 1,513 lives.

In 1996, a 1,865 square mile iceberg – twice the size of Luxembourg and large enough to supply one-fifth of the world's drinking water – broke off eastern Antarctica.

© *The Daily Mail*
September, 1997

Potential impacts on the countryside

Information from the Countryside Commission

Future sea-level rise and coastal response

The increase in temperature experienced over the past century will gradually lead to warming throughout the whole of the world's oceanic water. This will cause expansion of the ocean, and together with melting of glaciers and ice sheets will cause sea levels to rise. The IPCC prediction is for a rise of between 5-41 cm by 2050, with a most probable value of 21cm. Natural coasts will adjust to sea-level rise in complex ways, and although increased flooding and landward migration of coastal systems will occur in places, many natural coasts will prove surprisingly robust, especially where the supply of sediment to beaches from large or steep rivers and eroding cliffs is maintained.

Key points
- The predicted amount and rate of sea-level rise exceeds that experienced over the past 150 years. Rising sea levels are believed to be the main cause of an observed fall in beach levels across the globe.
- The rise in sea level, at least over the next 100 years, will not be so great as to change current problems at the coast, although these will be exacerbated.
- Low coasts subject to tidal flooding will become increasingly vulnerable unless defensive banks and walls are raised. Such improvements are most likely where large areas of land are threatened and/or where land and property values are high.
- Cliffs, especially in parts of eastern England and along the south coast where rocks are weak, will erode more rapidly, possibly up to three times the current rate of retreat.

Water balance and water resources

A warmer world will invigorate the hydrological cycle; more water will be evaporated from the oceans and more will fall as rain. The average increase by mid-century could be as high as 15 per cent. Unfortunately, at present, changes in precipitation cannot be forecast accurately, either by area or by season. However, it is certain that as warm season temperatures increase in the UK, summer evapotranspiration will increase and water deficits will become more common unless summer rainfall increases by an improbable amount. According to some scenarios, increased winter rain will improve on present aquifer recharge, but other forecasts suggest that a shorter winter may reduce aquifer recharge. For these reasons, future winter water balance is uncertain.

The overall picture of water balance in south and east England which emerges is one of summers with slightly less rainfall than today, but higher temperatures giving rise to increased potential evapotranspiration. The greater dryness of soils generally will probably lead to an increase in drought-tolerant species in areas of semi-natural vegetation such as grasslands, heaths and woodland.

Key points
- The potential impacts of reduced moisture reserves could be felt by soils and vegetation (including agricultural crops which are not irrigated), by rivers and aquifers, and thus by public water supply.
- If adverse changes occur, they will be most severe in the drier, eastern areas of lowland England. Western areas are likely to be even wetter and to have an increased water surplus.
- A warmer Britain will retain its current variable climate, so the main impacts of a reduction in water following increased evapotranspiration will be longer and more frequent periods of drought.
- The 1976 drought is estimated to be a one in 357 year event, but it could be a one in 14 year event by 2050. Other global models suggest similar conditions could occur even more frequently.
- Long-rooted vegetation (such as trees) can extract more water from soils than short-rooted vegetation (such as grass and most crops). As a result, it may be necessary to discourage afforestation over aquifers in the drier east.
- There is already concern about water extraction and its effect on water levels in ponds, rivers and wetlands, particularly in southern and eastern England. More frequent droughts could increase this concern and lead to calls to reduce reliance on local water reserves at such times.
- The demand from agriculture for irrigation water seems almost certain to rise, further increasing pressure on existing reserves, especially in dry periods.
- Water quality problems in both rivers and aquifers could

become more serious as a consequence of global warming.

- At the coast, existing zones of saline intrusion will tend to become more extensive, though more as an indirect result of changing water balance than as a direct consequence of sea-level rise, except on the most low-lying coasts.

Natural vegetation

The slow rate of changes in natural vegetation resulting from climate change will be very difficult to separate from the effects of other environmental pressures, including acid rain and ozone pollution. Nevertheless, we must expect appreciable changes since the rate at which climatic zones will migrate will exceed the natural rate of migration which can be achieved by many plants.

- Plant species with short life spans will tend to change their distribution as they adjust to new environmental conditions. Those near the limit of their range will be less able to adapt, as will those with slow rates of dispersal.
- Competition within plant communities will see some species benefiting from environmental change, while others, which are less effective competitors, will decline.
- Long-lived plants such as trees will be most affected as they will continue to try to grow in what may become increasingly un-satisfactory environments.
- Trees able to cope with disturbance (characteristically those that come early in the succession process) will be less affected than trees of mature woodland.
- The chilling requirement for bud burst will affect the response of individual trees to warmer springs.
- Climate change will allow certain introduced plant species (and domestic escapees) to survive and perhaps flourish. Certain insect and tick-borne diseases could become more common.
- The impact of ozone damage involves complex inter-relationships between air pollution, pests and host plants. Some pests are

stimulated by higher ozone episodes.
- Areas of importance for conservation over a wide geographical range are being affected by current rates of nitrogen deposition.
- The combination of acidification and coniferous afforestation can have a particularly severe effect in river catchments where soils are low in lime (podzols) and where rock weathers slowly.
- For all habitats at risk, the only long-term solution is a further major reduction in pollutant emissions based on the critical load concept.

Agriculture

While agriculture will be affected by climate change and other environmental variables, economic policies, technological advances and the efforts of plant breeders will continue to have a greater impact. This makes forecasts of future changes extremely difficult.

Key points
- Increased temperatures and a longer growing season will lead to falls of 5-10 per cent in wheat yields due to changes in water balance, but increases of 5-10 per cent in root crop yields. In many areas the latter will depend on continued supplies of irrigation water at low cost.
- Crops such as maize and sunflowers, which have already been

introduced to some parts of the countryside, will become more common and will spread further north.
- Pests will increase, especially with winters (which at present control population levels) becoming warmer.
- Although they cannot be forecast reliably, precipitation changes could be of far greater significance to agriculture than changes in temperature.
- Acid deposition is not generally a problem for agriculture, although, together with other forms of air pollution it could affect forestry.
- Many crops are relatively tolerant to increased UV-B levels, but some, such as barley, oats, sugar-beet and potatoes, are affected.
- The introduction of 15 per cent set-aside in 1992/1993 probably had a greater effect on agricultural production and the appearance of our countryside than any impacts expected as a result of climatic change over the next 60 years.

Recreation and tourism

If the impacts of environmental change on agriculture are difficult to separate from other influences, then this is even more true of recreation and tourism where individual decisions and social factors are the crucial determinants of action. Tourism in the UK has an international dimension which is sensitive to any change in climate that alters the competitive balance of holiday destinations. There are also push and pull effects: warmer summers may make the countryside more attractive to urban families, but transport policies may discourage long journeys, at least for day trips. Summer holidays in the Mediterranean may become less attractive if temperatures climb too high and the threat of skin cancer is taken more seriously.

Key points
- Increases in temperature are likely to stimulate an overall increase in tourism in the UK, with the greatest effects on activity holidays and some forms of outdoor recreation.
- A rise in sea temperatures will result in bathing in the sea becoming more popular and hence an increase in the use of beaches. At the same time beaches may be reduced in size by sea-level rise.
- Higher temperatures will encourage the uphill migration of enclosed agricultural land in UK uplands, threatening access for recreation.
- If future summers are drier as well as warmer, fire risk may restrict access to uplands, heaths and forests. Visitor management and

public information measures will need to respond to the increased fire risks.
- Rises in sea-level will affect fixed structures such as marinas and piers. Sea walls and promenades could be at risk. Coastal habitats used for recreation, such as sand dunes, beaches and saltmarshes, could also become more vulnerable.
- Ozone levels in rural areas may dissuade people from spending time at high altitudes on hot sunny days. Poor visibility caused by 'ozone smog' will affect people's enjoyment of the countryside.
- The increased risk of skin cancer due to reduced stratospheric ozone may result in changes in recreational behaviour, such as spending less time outdoors or wearing protective clothing or sun creams.

Impacts on human health

The interactions between stratospheric and tropospheric ozone changes have health implications which, together with the general effects of air pollution, are now beginning to be appreciated.

Key points
- Stratospheric ozone plays a critical role in cutting out the UV-B portion of solar radiation

which causes skin cancer in humans. However, most of the recent increase in human skin cancers is to be attributed to changes in lifestyle and behaviour (sunbathing, shorts, holidays in the sun), rather than to the recorded increase in UV-B at most latitudes.
- Ozone in the lower atmosphere is increasing steadily. While no more than an irritant to most people, future increases could cause more widespread health problems.
- EU requirements for publicity when high ozone episodes occur are likely to lead to increased public awareness of the UK ozone problem. In the same way, increasing publicity about precautions to be taken over UV-B exposure will increase awareness of the stratospheric ozone issue.
- Recent publicity over rises in diseases such as asthma are creating increasing concern about the impacts of declining air quality on health.

• The above is an extract from *Climate Change, Air Pollution and the English Countryside*, produced by the Countryside Commission. See page 41 for address details.

© Countryside Commission

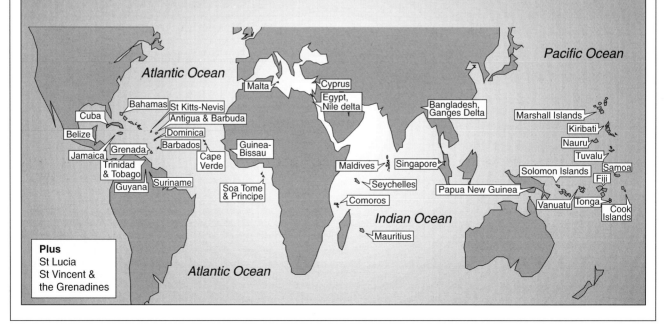

Big question of survival

Some of the 36 Alliance of Small Island States are so low-lying that they, plus the Ganges and Nile deltas in Bangladesh and Egypt, could be inundated in the next century by sea-level rise

Pacific Ocean

Atlantic Ocean

Malta

Cyprus

Egypt, Nile delta

Bangladesh, Ganges Delta

Marshall Islands

Bahamas

St Kitts-Nevis

Cuba

Antigua & Barbuda

Kiribati

Belize

Dominica

Nauru

Barbados

Tuvalu

Jamaica

Grenada

Guinea-Bissau

Maldives

Singapore

Solomon Islands

Samoa

Cape Verde

Trinidad & Tobago

Suriname

Seychelles

Papua New Guinea

Fiji

Guyana

Soa Tome & Principe

Comoros

Vanuatu

Tonga

Cook Islands

Indian Ocean

Mauritius

Plus
St Lucia
St Vincent & the Grenadines

Atlantic Ocean

Could global warming sink your holiday plans?

Climate change could ruin the appeal of Mediterranean resorts visited by British holiday makers, Greenpeace warns today. But if forecasts of famine, flood and drought come true, a decline in tourism could be the least of the problems, says Nicholas Schoon, Environment Correspondent

Shrinking beaches, water and food shortages could all become the norm around the Mediterranean, according to a Greenpeace report.

Commissioned from a freelance consultant, it has been timed for the run up to the Kyoto Climate Summit in Japan next month when nations will negotiate on what they must do to reduce climate change.

To try to beef it up for an audience of northern Europeans, whose governments are in the lead in advocating the toughest action to address the threat, Greenpeace is emphasising the threat to tourism.

More than 100 million people visit the sea's extensive, sunny coastline each year, and this has been projected to rise to as much as 340 million by 2025. 'Now this… is under threat as the possible impacts of climate change are more fully realised,' says Greenpeace. All the more reason to reduce the world's rising consumption of fossil fuels, emissions from which are changing the heat balance of the atmosphere.

The report is based on estimates for sea-level and temperature rises in the next century made by the UN's Intergovernmental Panel on Climate Change, which brings together most of the leading climatologists from around the world. But Greenpeace has chosen to emphasise its worst-case scenarios for 2100.

> **More than 100 million people visit the sea's extensive, sunny coastline each year, and this has been projected to rise to as much as 340 million by 2025**

Temperatures are expected to rise by up to 4°C over many inland areas. Annual rainfall is projected to fall by 10-40 per cent over much of Africa and south-eastern Spain with smaller but potentially significant changes elsewhere.

As oceans expand and glaciers melt in a warmer world, sea levels could rise by almost one metre by the end of the next century. Venice, the Nile Delta and Thessaloniki in Greece could witness sea-level rises 50 per cent higher, because they are already subsiding.

In Egypt it is estimated that a sea-level rise of only 0.5 metres would displace 16 per cent of the population if the coastline and riverbanks of the Nile Delta were not defended against the rising sea. Much of the population lives on the low-lying delta. Beach resorts could lose much of their sand.

Deserts may spread northwards and water resources will come under strain. Already Egypt, Libya, Tunisia, Algeria, Morocco and Syria have only about 1,000 cubic metres a year or less of water per person – a UN marker for water scarcity.

Yields of grain and other crops could suffer because of droughts. Livestock production will also suffer because of deterioration of grazing land. One study predicts large parts of Spain, southern Italy and Greece could become unsuitable for cereal growing.

Warmer conditions are likely to increase cases of malaria, schistosomiasis, yellow fever and dengue fever. *© The Independent November, 1997*

Britain calls for US action on climate

Climate change threatens to swamp small Pacific Islands. But industrial countries are fighting shy of the action needed to prevent it. America, Australia and Japan must do more, argues Derek Fatchett, Minister of State at the Foreign and Commonwealth Office

I have recently returned from the Pacific. Not the newly industrialised Pacific Rim which dominates the financial pages, but the heart of the region – the small island states of the South Pacific.

For us in Britain, climate change and global warming might seem remote. For those living in the South Pacific islands, the issue is literally one of survival.

The question there is not whether grapes might grow in the Pennines. It is simply and starkly: 'will my country exist in fifty years' time?' This was brought home to me very sharply: in Rarotonga, the hotel I stayed in would be one of the first buildings to disappear as the sea rises.

I was there for the Conference of the South Pacific Forum States. You would think at least in that context you would find a sense of urgency and purpose about climate change. Indeed the smallest and most vulnerable islands, who risk losing their coastal plains or even their very existence, had it at the top of their agenda. It was the response of their developed country partners which was so disturbing.

In eight weeks' time the nations of the world will meet in Kyoto to decide how we will take the first steps to prevent potentially catastrophic climate change. The EU has proposed a 15 per cent reduction by developed countries of the gases which cause the greenhouse effect by 2010. The UK has set itself a domestic target of a 20 per cent reduction in carbon dioxide. It is not an easy target, but it is one which will require major changes in lifestyle or industrial technology. At the very worst it may have a marginal effect on economic growth. At best it may stimulate new environmental technologies and industries and create new growth.

The response by some of our western partners has been disappointing to say the least. The Japanese have just published their proposals under which developed countries as a whole would be required to achieve emissions reductions of around three per cent. Whilst it's welcome that the Japanese are now talking about hard numbers, three per cent is too low to be a credible response. But at least we now have something to negotiate about.

Meanwhile, we hope the US position will emerge soon following this week's meeting at the White House. The Administration's heart is in the right place. But it will have to work hard to overcome the doubts in Congress and elsewhere, where many refuse even to recognise there is a problem.

But in the Pacific, where the problems caused by global warming will be most keenly felt, the response has been more disappointing. While the rest of us discuss reductions in emissions, the Australian Govern-

ment talks about increases. Measures to cut emissions are seen as too costly or difficult.

I find it hard to believe that Australia, one of the richest countries in the world with an average emissions level second only to the US, cannot do better than this.

Here in Britain, we have already reduced our emissions from 1990 levels and meet the commitments we signed at Rio. To go beyond this to achieve our 20 per cent target will require further efforts in areas like transport, domestic energy efficiency, power generation and industrial processes. We are preparing our strategy to announce next year.

We are also sharing our thinking with the Australian Government. What is needed is the political will to explain to the public why action must be taken and ask them to do the right thing. If I know the Australian people, I am sure they will respond.

Tony Blair sent a strong message to leaders at the June UN Environment Meeting. He said that we would be failing our children if we did not tackle climate change. Some of the key countries have so far turned a deaf ear. I urge them to listen to the concerns of the small vulnerable states represented at the South Pacific Forum.

Some of the poorest people in other large developing countries, like India, China and Bangladesh, will also be affected by rising sea levels. Large parts of Africa may be affected by regular droughts. This is a major test for the post cold-war world order. Real political leadership is needed.

© *The Independent*
October, 1997

Global warming poses new threat to whales' survival

By Charles Arthur, Science Editor

Save the krill' may not yet have the resonance of 'save the whale' as a rallying cry. But new findings by scientists in the Antarctic suggest that global warming is effectively killing off the tiny shrimp-like creatures which are the favourite food of many species of whales, including the blue, grey, humpback and minke.

The krill population is being undermined by salps, simple pouch-like creatures that are eaten by only a few marine animals, but which produce dense blooms which interfere with krill reproduction and kill off their larvae.

Krill look like small prawns, with a pair of swimming legs and large black eyes. They grow up to about 6 centimetres long during their life of between five and 10 years, maturing after two years. There are estimated to be about 500,000 billion individual krill – comprising 500 million tonnes of biomass – and they occur in vast swarms which can seem to turn the water red. They have been harvested since the 1970s by Russia, the Ukraine and Japan, with about 300,000 tonnes caught annually: their uses include feed for fish farms, domestic animals and human food.

By contrast, salp only live about a year, and their numbers can explode if conditions are favourable.

Data collection in the Antarctic suggests that there are fewer krill because salps flourish in years when there is less sea ice, whereas the krill do better in colder years – probably because they can live off algae that forms on the ice. Krill form food for predators including 'baleen' whales – the class of whale with a sieve-like mouth for filtering food from the ocean – as well as Adélie penguins, petrels, fulmars, squid and fish.

Over the past 50 years, records show that there have been progressively fewer winters with extensive sea-ice coverage, while average air temperatures have risen. This will help the salp and hurt the krill. That, in turn, will affect the marine food web, and could lead to falling numbers of whales.

At the same time, on King George Island in the Antarctic the number of Adelie penguins – which forage for young krill – has fallen by 30 per cent since the 1970s, and fewer fledglings are surviving.

© The Independent
June, 1997

Birds of a weather

Global warming puts cuckoo's clock forward. By David Derbyshire, Science Correspondent

Global warming means nature lovers could soon be hearing the first cuckoo of winter rather than spring, say experts.

Britain's birds are laying their first eggs of the year earlier than at the start of the 1970s, new research has revealed.

Scientists claim it is more proof that the warming of the atmosphere is shifting the seasons, and that spring is arriving sooner each year.

Humphrey Crick, of the British Trust for Ornithology, believes climatic upheaval is the cause of the 'startling change' in the habits of birds.

'When the birds in our gardens are changing their behaviour, it is time to believe global warming is happening,' said Mr Crick, who headed the research team.

'If it goes on like this, you will be talking about the first cuckoo of winter, never mind spring.'

Researchers studied more than 74,000 egg-laying records from 65 species between 1971 and 1995.

By the end of the period, 20 had brought forward their first clutch of eggs by between four and 17 days. Only the stock dove was laying significantly later.

On average, the 20 earliest birds were laying 8.8 days sooner in 1995 than in 1971.

The biggest change was seen in the magpie, which brought its egg-laying forward by 17 days, followed by the corn bunting (16 days), the chiff chaff (14 days) and the redshank, redstart and long-tailed tit (all 11 days).

The report, in *Nature* magazine, adds to the mounting evidence that the world's climate is changing.

In April, scientists revealed that the first buds of spring appeared a week earlier in 1991 than in 1981, and that plants are now blooming longer in the autumn.

This year spring was at least three weeks early.

© The Daily Mail
August, 1997

The biggest thaw

The world is in the grip of the biggest thaw since the end of the last ice age. Information from the World Wide Fund for Nature (WWF-UK)

The big thaw

There is growing evidence that the world is in the grip of the biggest thaw since the end of the last ice age some 10,000 years ago. It is the most unambiguous signal yet of the impact of pollution on the planet's climate. We have hit the defrost button from the Arctic to the Himalayas, the Alps to the southern seas.

The Arctic, says climatologist Betsy Weathered, of the University of Colorado, 'may be the most dynamic and responsive region in Earth to climate change'.

In 1995, the UK Meteorological Office reported that much of Siberia was 3°C warmer than earlier this century. Arctic soils have warmed by up to 4°C. Average temperatures at nine North American weather stations in the Arctic have risen by 5°C since 1968. Much of the Arctic Ocean has warmed by 1°C or more since 1987, and more than 5 per cent of its sea ice has disappeared in the past 15 years.

The Arctic climate is known to be naturally variable, but such changes are unprecedented. European researchers have examined a thousand-year record of summer temperatures preserved in the annual rings of Siberian larches, and found that average summer temperatures have been at their highest during the 20th century. 'The trend seems to be accelerating. Tree growth in the Urals is exploding. It does suggest a major warming,' says team head Keith Briffa of the University of East Anglia in England.

The thaw is triggering major ecological impacts throughout the Arctic. In the Arctic National Wildlife Refuge in Alaska, for instance, the porcupine caribou herd, which currently numbers 150,000, goes north to calf each spring. Once, the migration coincided with maxi-

mum plant growth in the refuge. Now, even though the herds move earlier in the year, the grasses have often gone to seed before they arrive on Alaska's North Slope.

Permanently frozen land, known as permafrost, is melting in Siberia, Canada and Alaska, causing chaos in city and countryside alike. The permafrost zone has moved up to 100 kilometres north in parts of Canada in the past century. Thawing permafrost is already causing roads and buildings to subside, railway lines to buckle and clumps of trees to fall into sink holes in many parts of the Arctic.

At the other end of the Earth, the map of Antarctica is changing. The Antarctic peninsula, which juts north towards South America, has warmed by 2.5°C in 40 years. Many of the large floating ice shelves connected to the peninsula are breaking loose and melting. Two-thirds of the Wordie ice sheet – an area the size of Luxembourg – have disappeared in 30 years. A 1,300-square kilometre section of the nearby Larsen A shelf collapsed and broke into thousands of icebergs in 1995. Its companion, Larsen B, is riddled with cracks and faces a similar fate. As the ice sheets

warm, they reach a critical temperature above which they rapidly collapse and float away.

On the islands of the Antarctic peninsula, the Adélie penguin population has declined in the past 20 years as the sea ice, from which they feed, has retreated. At Campbell Island, rockhopper penguins have declined by more than 90 per cent. Other mysterious disappearances include sea lions from around the Falkland Islands and elephant seals from the South Shetland Islands – probably because the warmer water is driving away food such as krill, a kind of shrimp. Researchers reported in mid-1997 that krill populations had collapsed due to warming.

Melting ice is now a global phenomenon, and glacier melt is one of the best indications that the climate is getting warmer. Europe's Alpine glaciers have lost half their volume since 1850 as the region has warmed, according to Wilfried Haeberli of Zurich University, director of the UN's World Glacier Monitoring Service. Typical is the Grüben glacier on the slopes of Fletschhorn in southern Switzerland. It has been melting since the middle of the last century, but the retreat has dramatically accelerated during the 1990s. Today its toe is 200 metres further up the mountain than at the start of the decade. 'There is no doubt that world-wide warming is responsible for this,' says Haeberli. In neighbouring Austria, 90 per cent of glaciers show 'substantial' retreat. As glaciers retreat they have caused intense chemical weathering of rocks, creating a dramatic flush of pollution into lakes, says Roland Psenner of the University of Innsbruck. Sulphate pollution, normally associated with acid rain, has increased fourfold in some Alpine lakes.

In Alaska, the Columbia Glacier, a river of ice covering 1,100 square kilometres, has retreated by 3 kilometres in the past 15 years. And the 5,000 square kilometre Bering Glacier, the world's largest temperate glacier, has retreated by 10 kilometres this century, with losses reaching an astounding one kilometre a year in the 1990s. Further south, Paradise Glacier, in Washington State's Mount Rainier National Park, is receding, and in Glacier National Park, Montana, many small glaciers have disappeared in the past 30 years. Dan Fagre of the US Geological Service predicts there will be no glaciers in Glacier National Park by 2030.

Tropical glaciers are also melting fast. In Africa, the volume of ice on Mount Kenya has decreased by 40 per cent since 1963. Similar retreats are occurring in the Venezuelan and Peruvian Andes, where the speed of retreat has increased sevenfold since the start of the 1980s. Glaciers around Mount Jaya in Irian Jaya, part of the island of New Guinea, have shrunk from 19 square kilometres to 3 square kilometres since 1936.

Melting can be lethal, making firm ice brittle, unleashing rock falls and creating large water lakes near glaciers. Glacial lake overflow has already become more frequent in the Himalayas because of global warming. Residents of the Nepalese village of Manjo, near Mount Everest and just outside Sagarmatha National Park, live in fear of a massive burst from Imja lake. Says geomorphologist Telji Watanabe, from Japan's Hokkaido University, 'It's very dangerous. Very simple calculations say that there will be an outburst at Imja lake in the next five to six years.'

Tipping the balance of the tropics

Tropical temperatures are rising, says David Rind of NASA's Goddard Institute of Space Studies in New York. Indeed, temperature changes in the tropics were the single largest reason for the surge in global average temperatures during the 1980s. The tropics are also becoming drier, especially in the already arid regions

stretching east from the Sahel in Africa, as far as Indonesia.

Since the mid-1960s, average rainfall in the Sahel and much of the east and south of Africa has declined sharply. The past decade in southern Africa has been both the warmest and driest this century. The growing seasons of 1991-92 and 1994-95 were among the five driest years this century, causing crop failures, water shortages, killing wildlife and threatening human health.

In the oceans, damage to coral reefs appears to be increasing as ocean waters throughout the tropics become warmer. Coral reefs die off if the water becomes too warm. A rise in temperature of 1°C for four weeks will cause many corals to expel the microalgae that live in their cells. The algae provide the coral with both their coloration and their food. The process, called coral bleaching, became increasingly common in the Caribbean and South Pacific as oceans warmed in the 1980s. By the 1990s there were around 10 bleaching events a year, affecting 20 countries. Usually the coral recovers in the following cool season, but if all algae are lost the coral will die. Some Galapagos reefs hit by bleaching in 1983 have yet to recover.

The tropical oceans, Rind says, were up to 0.75°C warmer during the 1980s than in the previous three decades. This appears to have affected the intensity and frequency of the largest single influence on tropical climate – a cyclical weather phenomenon called El Niño in the tropical Pacific Ocean. El Niño events typically occur every three or four years, when the winds and currents across the equatorial Pacific switch direction, pushing a pool of

very warm water out east across the Pacific towards the Americas. After about nine months, the reverse currents falter and the system returns to its normal state.

In recent years, El Niños have become more frequent, intense and devastating. El Niño has brought droughts to Australia and Indonesia, and heavy rains and floods to the normally arid western shores of the Americas, from Peru to California. El Niño has also coincided with intense droughts in India, north-east Brazil and much of Africa, and with torrential rains in Japan and the eastern Mediterranean. During June 1997, dramatic increases in water temperature were recorded in the Pacific Ocean, signalling what many scientists believe may turn out to be the strongest El Niño this century.

Two decades of frequent and intense El Niño events, coupled with a near-continuos warming of the tropical Pacific Ocean, is, statistically, a once in 2,000 year event, according to Kevin Trenberth of the US Government's National Center for Atmospheric Research in Boulder, Colorado, and may well have been caused by global warming.

The ecological and economic effects of major El Niños are massive. In 1982 and 1983, El Niño caused the collapse of one of the world's most valuable anchovy fisheries off Peru, starving a quarter of the country's seals and leaving fishermen's nets empty. It triggered forest fires in Borneo that covered an area the size of Belgium; typhoons were diverted onto new tracks, crashing into Hawaii and Tahiti; Australia had its worst drought for a century and experienced massive wildfires; Galapagos had more rain in two weeks than the previous six years; California and the southern US faced record storms and floods. Overall, the loss to the world economy from this one weather phenomenon was put at more than $13 billion.

• The above is an extract from *State of the Climate – A time for action*, produced by WWF. See page 41 for address details.

© WWF

Global warming

Information from the Young People's Trust for the Environment and Nature Conservation

Introduction

Global warming is the increase of average world temperatures as a result of what is known as the greenhouse effect. Certain gases in the atmosphere act like glass in a greenhouse, allowing sunlight through to heat the earth's surface but trapping the heat as it radiates back into space. As the greenhouse gases build up in the atmosphere the earth gets hotter.

Causes

One of the main greenhouse gases is carbon dioxide (CO_2). As trees grow they take in CO_2 from the air. When the wood dies the CO_2 is returned to the air. Forest clearance and wood burning (such as happens in tropical rain forests) is increasing the latter half of the process, adding to the CO_2 in the atmosphere. Deforestation is now out of control. For example in 1987 an area of the Amazon rain forest the size of Britain was burned, adding 500 million tonnes of CO_2 to the atmosphere. The loss of the forests also means that there are fewer trees to absorb CO_2.

The recent fires in Indonesia, with more than a million hectares of forest ablaze thanks to fires set deliberately by logging companies, are likely to have an effect on global climate, but the more immediate effect has been the cloud of smog which enveloped much of south-east Asia during September and early October 1997.

However, as large a contribution as deforestation makes, it causes less than half the yearly total of CO_2, the rest comes from the burning of coal, oil and other fossil fuels. These fossil fuels are burned in cars, power stations and factories of the wealthier nations such as the USA and Western Europe.

Televisions, lights and computers use electricity that is created mainly from burning coal. Every time we switch on a light we are adding to the greenhouse effect. Cars are also major sources of CO_2. The average European is responsible for nearly 2.5 times as much atmospheric carbon as a Latin American. The concentration of CO_2 has increased 25% since the industrial revolution, half of this rise has been in the last 30 years. It is expected to double within decades.

Other greenhouse gases

CO_2 contributes about 50% to the greenhouse effect. The other greenhouse gases are methane, chlorofluorocarbons (CFCs) and nitrous oxide (N_2O).

Methane – is released during coal-mining activities, oil exploration and when vegetation is burnt during land clearance. The main source of methane though is agricultural activity. It is released from wetlands such as rice paddies and from animals, particularly cud-chewing species like cows. The problem with methane is that as the world population increases, agricultural activity must increase and so emissions of methane will also increase. Since the 1960s the amount of methane in the air has increased by 1% per year – twice as fast as the build up of CO_2.

Nitrous oxide – comes from both natural and man-made processes. Man-influenced sources, which represent about 45% of output to the atmosphere, are mainly: fossil fuel combustion, as in power stations; use of nitrogenous fertilisers; burning rain forests and human and animal waste. N_2O contributes about 6% to the greenhouse effect at the moment.

CFCs – found in fridges, air conditioners, aerosols etc., are extremely effective greenhouse gases. Although there are lower concentrations of CFCs in the atmosphere than CO_2 they trap more heat. A CFC molecule is 10,000 times more effective in trapping heat than a CO_2 molecule, methane is about 30 times more effective. Methane molecules survive for 10 years in the atmosphere and CFCs for 110 years. It is this that causes people to want to ban them completely.

Feedback processes

CO_2 – about half the CO_2 released by burning fossil fuels is absorbed by the oceans. It is taken up by minute sea creatures or dragged to the ocean depths by the circulation of water. Recent research suggests that as the earth heats up, the oceans will be less efficient in absorbing CO_2, leaving more in the atmosphere and so adding further to global warming.

Methane – as global temperatures become greater, so large quantities of methane stored in the frozen tundra of the north may be released. Also methane trapped in the sea bed may be freed by temperature rises.

As the world warms it causes feedback processes. Increases in temperature cause the liberation of CO_2 and methane which then cause further warming. Another feedback mechanism arises through higher air temperatures evaporating more water and so providing more cloud which both traps heat from below and reflects back sunlight from above. As the world warms, the effect of clouds could become more and more significant.

Effects

If no action is taken the greenhouse effect could lead to a rise in average global temperatures of between 1.5-

4.5°C as early as the year 2030. These rises will be greater towards the poles and less at the tropics. There will also be more warming in winter than summer.

Such increases will make the world hotter than it has been for more than 100,000 years. The rise will also be faster than ever before; a rise of 3°C after the last ice age took thousands of years. By the end of next century temperatures could have reached those of the time of the dinosaurs and it is doubtful if humans could survive. The effects are already showing – the ten hottest years since the 1860s have been in the last 15 years.

Storms – storms and hurricanes will become more frequent and stronger as oceans heat up causing more water to evaporate. Evidence is building up at an alarming rate. In September 1991 Japan was hit by Typhoon Mireille, its worst for 30 years. Then in September 1993 it was hit by Typhoon Yancy – the 13th that year, and the worst for 50 years. In January 1993 barometric pressure around Shetland dropped to its lowest recorded level, 915 millibars. The oil tanker Braer broke up in the resulting storm. In March 1993 the 'Storm of the Century' hit America, causing $1.6 billion in damage from Canada to Cuba. In December 1993 hurricane-force storms caused Britain its worst flooding for 40 years.

Droughts – continental heartlands will dry out more in summer. In 1988 the US suffered its worst heatwave and drought for 50 years. It cannot be proved that this was due to the greenhouse effect but it does give us some idea of what to expect in the future.

Floods – sea levels are already rising at a rate of 1 to 2mm each year due to expansion of the top layer of the oceans as they warm and the melting of the polar ice caps. The predicted rise by 2050 is between 20 and 50cm. This will cause increased flooding in coastal areas and river estuaries such as Bangladesh and the Nile Delta. London and many other British coastal cities will be threatened also. It is now a priority to strengthen Britain's sea defences.

What can be done?

It is important to slow the warming as much as possible. This means using less fossil fuel, eliminating CFCs altogether, and slowing down deforestation.

This can be achieved best through energy conservation, including better use of public transport and cleaner, more efficient cars; and energy efficiency by greater use of gas which produces less CO_2 than coal and oil, and through renewable energy such as solar power. We need to stop destroying rain forests (deforestation) and start replanting trees (afforestation) to soak up carbon dioxide.

A United Nations panel has estimated that we need to reduce global fuel use by 60% immediately in order to stabilise the climate. Current commitments by those governments participating in CO_2 reduction will only lower global CO_2 by 4-6%. Although the developed industrialised nations still produce most CO_2, the rapidly developing nations of South America and Asia are increasing their CO_2 production at a much higher rate, and by 2010 they will overtake the West as the main producers of CO_2.

The developing countries are reluctant to participate in any CO_2 emission reduction plans, arguing that they did not create global warming and that it is the responsibility of developed countries to cut their own emissions or to support developing countries with financial aid. Oil-producing countries – including a significant lobby in the

US – are also reluctant to have their sales reduced and have protested against action on climate change.

Nuclear power – does not produce CO_2 so could replace other forms of energy. It is necessary, though, to find an effective means of safely disposing of the radioactive waste that can remain dangerous for hundreds to thousands of years.

Alternative energy – more funding is required for research and development of alternative pollution-free energy sources such as solar, wave and wind energy.

How can you help?

Ignorance – is a root cause that you can help end by telling your friends and family about the problems.
Energy – encourage people to use less electricity by insulating lofts and windows for example.
Trees – recycle paper, plant trees, avoid tropical hardwoods that don't have a 'good wood seal'.
Transport – ask your family to avoid using private transport through car sharing, public transport and by using a bicycle for shorter trips.
CFCs – we can all help by using CFC-free aerosols.

Perhaps the following statements may help to inspire you . . .
'Nobody made a greater mistake than he who did nothing because he could do only a little.'

Edmund Burke

'It is time that we realised that we all share a common future.'
Gro Harlem Brundtland, Prime Minister of Norway, 1988

References:

Our Common Future – The World Commission on Environment & Development. (Oxford Press, 1987)
The Greenhouse Effect – Stuart Boyle & John Ardill (Hodder & Stoughton, 1989)
BBC Wildlife Magazine – Volume 7, number 6.
Friends of the Earth, *Disappearing Rain Forest* – R. Prosser, Considering Conservation (Dryad Press, 1987)

Wildlife drowning under the high seas

East coast nature reserves sinking fast into the sea, threatening birds in wetlands. By Nicholas Schoon, Environment Correspondent

Some of Britain's best known nature reserves will be drowned under the sea in the next few decades, conservation organisations warned yesterday.

It was their opening shot in a war to persuade the Government to come up with more money and change its coastal defence planning in order to save, or recreate, precious seaside habitats in East Anglia that are home to rare species such as the bearded tit, bittern and wainscot moth, and which are under mounting threat.

The Government themselves forecast that the sea level around south-east England will rise by nearly two feet over the next half century. This is partly because the entire south-east portion of the British Isles is slowly sinking by one or two millimetres a year as the land mass readjusts to the removal of the ice caps at the end of the last Ice Age. The other reason is that the oceans are predicted to expand and rise due to man-made global warming.

The conservation groups, which include the Royal Society for the Protection of Birds, the National Trust and English Heritage, say that a wildlife-rich chain of low-lying grazing marshes, reedbeds and lagoons behind the shingle beaches of Suffolk and Norfolk are at risk. Well known for their birds, they are all designated by the Government for nature protection and several are meant to be protected by European Union nature conservation laws.

In February last year a combination of storms and exceptionally high tides flooded the freshwater Cley and Salthouse Marshes in Norfolk with salt water to a depth of six feet along a two-mile stretch of coast. The marine flooding lasted for three weeks.

The marshes there are one of the few UK haunts of the bittern, a large heron-like bird which is one of the most critically endangered in Britain. No bitterns bred there in 1996 because the salt stunted the reeds which give them cover and killed the freshwater fish they eat. Fortunately Cley and Salthouse are now recovering, and two bittern nests have been seen this summer.

> ### The Government themselves forecast that the sea level around south-east England will rise by nearly two feet over the next half century

John Sharpe of the RSPB said: 'Some of Europe's finest wildlife sites are being lost. If these sites cannot be protected in the longer term then replacement habitats must be created. There is no clear mechanism or adequate money available to ensure this happens – the Government needs to address this urgently.'

Peter Doktor, of the Norfolk Wildlife Trust, said that at Cley and Salthouse Marshes the Government's Environment Agency – responsible for coastal defences – had now decided to build an earthen embankment as an extra line of defence behind the natural shingle bank. This was welcome.

But at the trust's Brancaster Marshes, the agency was promoting 'managed retreat' which means not maintaining the coastal defences and letting the sea gradually move inland.

The wildlife campaigners accept that there are places where the best policy may be not to build or maintain expensive coastal defences, but to let the sea have its way. However, they want new wetland habitats to be created to replace those areas which are lost to the waves – and since that will usually involve taking farmland out of production this would not come cheap.

© The Independent
August, 1997

The planet's hottest problem

Why are politicians lagging so far behind when we know the earth is already getting warmer? By Paul Brown

In ancient times there was just one politician who fiddled while Rome burned. Today, as the whole Earth begins to heat up and the climate changes before our eyes, world leaders are reaching for their violins in droves. Politicians admit that they can see the flames – or, to put it their way, they accept that the scientists' warnings about global warming are proving correct. Yet their reactions continue to be far from adequate.

This week President Bill Clinton called a White House conference to prepare the United States public to bite the bullet on carbon dioxide reductions. The World Bank is holding a meeting to try to move governments on the issue: and in 10 days' time the 160 nations which signed the Climate Change Convention at the Earth Summit in 1992 enter the final round of negotiations in Bonn to seek action on climate change beyond the year 2000. But even if the most far-reaching suggestions on the table in Bonn are accepted – which is unlikely – the politicians' action is so far behind the scientists' demands that a series of climatic disasters seems almost inevitable.

The scientists are more united in their views than ever before. Action is needed quickly, they say: according to the Intergovernmental Panel on Climate Change, a 60 per cent reduction on current carbon dioxide emissions is urgently required to save the world from dangerous climate change.[1] Note the word 'dangerous'. They point to evidence (which President Clinton has stated several times that he accepts) that the world is already heating up, currently by 0.1°C a decade; and if the process speeds up, then natural systems will not be able to adapt.

In Canada, fir trees are already measurably dying back: an indication that the vast forests of the US, Canada and Russia will die in the heat before the next generations of saplings can establish themselves on the cooler northern edge of the forest. Another newly detected problem – predicted, but not expected so soon

> **A 60 per cent reduction on current carbon dioxide emissions is urgently required to save the world from dangerous climate change**

– is the slowing down of the mighty Gulf Stream which warms the west of the British Isles. This is caused by melting ice from Greenland, and the slow-down threatens Britain with more stormy and sometimes colder winter weather: Sir Robert May, the Government's chief scientific adviser, recently described this prospect as awesome.[2]

The United States is also being made aware of the urgency of the situation, not least because the most likely consequence of inaction is world-wide economic recession. Yesterday in Washington at the World Bank conference there were dire warnings about the effect on the world economy of the current El Niño weather pattern. This is the movement of extra warm water from

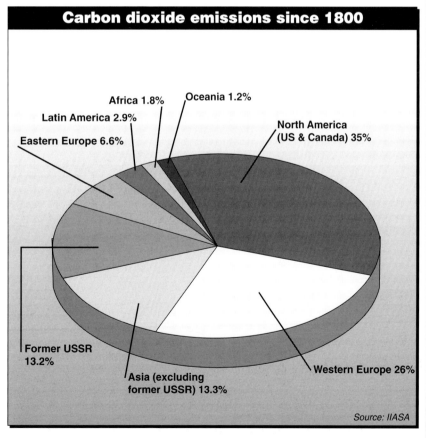

Carbon dioxide emissions since 1800

- Africa 1.8%
- Oceania 1.2%
- Latin America 2.9%
- Eastern Europe 6.6%
- North America (US & Canada) 35%
- Former USSR 13.2%
- Asia (excluding former USSR) 13.3%
- Western Europe 26%

Source: IIASA

west to east in the Pacific, enough to disrupt trade winds and weather patterns over more than half the world. This year's El Niño is causing the drought which is allowing the Indonesian fires to burn out of control.

El Niño is already causing droughts and storms in South America. The World Bank conference was told yesterday that it was going to cause economic disruption through the Asia Pacific region and South America for the next 12 to 18 months.

Other science published yesterday shows that much of the frozen soil that underpins Alaska is melting. The permafrost acts as a foundation for roads, railways, and oil pipelines. It also holds together mountains which would otherwise crack open and cause landslides. Temperatures in Alaska are rising three times faster than in the rest of the Arctic. Roads, building foundations and airport runways built on the permafrost are crumbling. China is watching anxiously: it has 2,000 miles of railways built on the edge of the permafrost zone, all of which will need new foundations.

The solution is clear: carbon dioxide emissions need to be cut, with urgency and on a global level. Carbon dioxide, although making up only a tiny percentage of air, acts as a barrier to prevent heat escaping. As with the glass in a greenhouse, it lets in the sunlight and prevents the heat getting out – hence the 'greenhouse effect'. There are other greenhouse gases, such as methane, but carbon dioxide is the single most difficult problem because it stays in the atmosphere for up to 100 years before being reabsorbed by plants or the oceans. All that time it adds to the heating up of the Earth.

What makes it possible to set targets for cuts is the fact that carbon dioxide production can be measured. We know how much coal is burned in power stations and how much petrol goes into cars, and each nation's extra carbon dioxide can be calculated. Hence it is easy to pinpoint blame for global warming and police its control.

Targets, however, are what the world cannot currently agree on. The

---

'We are fast approaching the point where the Earth's physical and biological systems will not be able to meet our demands'

European Union, the most advanced of the big power blocks on climate change, has offered a 15 per cent reduction in greenhouse-gas emissions by 2010. Japan this week offered 5 per cent, but after much agonising – because Japan hosts the meeting in Kyoto, from December 1 to 10, where 160 heads of state are due to sign the final deal on climate change for the first 20 years of the next century.

The Japanese government wants the talks to succeed, but is facing heavy pressure from its industry lobby not to concede too much. But the United States is key to the success or failure of these deliberations. At the Earth Summit review conference in New York in June, President Clinton promised both legally binding targets and timetables in Kyoto. So far he has been unable to deliver, because of the powerful industry lobby that fears action on global warming will put up taxes and cost them business. The lobby spent £10 million in six weeks on television advertisements which claimed that action on global warming would mean higher taxes and job losses.

China and the other G77 nations argue that the US, as the

world's largest carbon dioxide emitter, is, with the rest of the industrialised world, the main cause of the problem. The US has yet to offer anything beyond the turn of the century, and has not kept its previous promises to peg to 1990 levels by the year 2000. It is already due to overshoot the 2000 target by 14 per cent.[3]

Yet whatever compromise is reached, the problem will certainly not wait for politicians. Dr Bob Watson, director of the World Bank's environment department and former environment adviser in President Clinton's executive, yesterday put it this way: 'We are fast approaching the point where the Earth's physical and biological systems will not be able to meet our demands for environmental goods and services on which we depend. Nations are already facing threats to their most basic development goals.'

This is the World Bank speaking, not Greenpeace. Another straw in the wind was the appearance in London this week of John Browne, chief executive of BP, on the same platform as Chris Rose, campaigns director of Greenpeace. Mr Browne acknowledged that the greenhouse effect was real and made great play of the fact that BP was investing in solar power. The company sees a business opportunity: two billion people currently without electricity live in sunny areas. On cutting the use of fossil fuels he was a little circumspect. There was plenty of time for that – meanwhile the world wanted to own cars, driven by oil, and they must be given that opportunity.

Still, a deal is almost certain to be stitched up. World leaders will want to hail it as a historic step towards saving the world from climate change. But if the evidence piling up is correct, it certainly will not be enough.

Sources: (1) The UN's Inter-governmental Panel on Climate Change, 1996; (2) Sir Robert May's scientific report on Climate Change to the Prime Minister, October 1997; (3) US Department of Energy, Oct 1997. © *The Guardian* *October, 1997*

Now the test for Kyoto resolution

Seen in the harsh light of dawn, what did more than a week of round-the-clock negotiation in Kyoto achieve? Nicholas Schoon, Environment Correspondent, examines the brave new world created by the new anti-global warming treaty

Things will never be the same again . . . perhaps. In Kyoto the nations of the world agreed on a decisive step to begin tackling the threat of man-made climate change. But it will take about six years before you can judge whether nearly 30 developed nations – which agreed to cut their annual output of six key global-warming gases – are serious about the new Kyoto protocol.

First, they will have to sign and ratify the treaty to make it legally binding – and there are major doubts about whether the biggest polluter, the US, with its anti-Kyoto majority of politicians in Congress, will.

Secondly, their governments will have to make a prompt start on implementing the policies needed to stop emissions of these gases rising. They have a few years to change the upward trend into a decline in order to comply with the provisions of the new United Nations treaty.

Overall, it means a 5.2 per cent cut in annual emissions of climate-changing greenhouse gases from the developed world by 2012, compared with a 1990 baseline. The European Union has agreed to an 8 per cent cut, the US to 7 per cent and Japan to 6 per cent. Although EU nations felt strongly that the US and Japan should cut emissions with the same flat rate, the fact that they took the issue most seriously and called for a deeper cut than any other group of countries has ended up with them being allocated the largest reduction.

As for Japan, its negotiators argued remorselessly and successfully in Kyoto that the nation hosting the treaty conference was a special case. Japan uses fossil fuels with high efficiency because it has virtually none of its own – they all have to be imported. As a result, it produces relatively few of the greenhouse gas emissions associated with these fuels considering its huge productivity and wealth. Under the final agreement, Russia has to stabilise its emissions. Australia, Iceland, and Norway are allowed to increase their global-warming pollution by 2012; they all pleaded successfully that they were special cases.

Environmentalists are, discreetly, rather pleased by the final agreement. Given how far the major industrialised nations were apart at the start of the conference, the depth of cuts agreed is slightly more than they were guessing at its start.

It was the Americans who caved in most of all, but there is a risk the Republican-dominated Congress will refuse to ratify the treaty. Jeremy Leggett, a former campaigner with Greenpeace who now promotes solar power, said: 'I'm quite encouraged. Now we'll see whether this treaty starts to transform the energy industry.' He said it sent a clear signal to big oil companies that their sales of polluting fossil fuels would be capped in the developed world, and encouraged them to move into renewable energy sources. In the long run, the developing countries will have to be brought into the treaty if it is to be effective in slowing the rate of climate change caused by pollution.

The most rational way of dealing with the problem seems to be the 'contraction and convergence' approach advocated by the London-based Global Commons Institute. Under its scenario, every inhabitant of the planet would be allocated the same quantity of greenhouse gases to emit, divided out of a total which kept climate change within tolerable limits.

This would give every country, whatever its wealth, a certain quota of pollution. Developed countries have more than their fair share of this quota, while many developing nations still have less. The institute says all countries should be able to trade their quotas through a free market.

© *The Independent December, 1997*

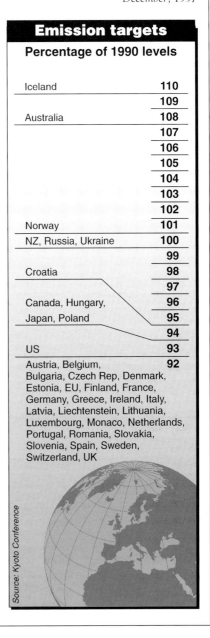

Emission targets

Percentage of 1990 levels

Country	%
Iceland	110
	109
Australia	108
	107
	106
	105
	104
	103
	102
Norway	101
NZ, Russia, Ukraine	100
	99
Croatia	98
	97
Canada, Hungary,	96
Japan, Poland	95
	94
US	93
Austria, Belgium, Bulgaria, Czech Rep, Denmark, Estonia, EU, Finland, France, Germany, Greece, Ireland, Italy, Latvia, Liechtenstein, Lithuania, Luxembourg, Monaco, Netherlands, Portugal, Romania, Slovakia, Slovenia, Spain, Sweden, Switzerland, UK	92

Source: Kyoto Conference

Is the Government's target for greenhouse gas just so much hot air?

The Government says Britain will cut its carbon dioxide pollution by 20 per cent by 2010. Nicholas Schoon asks if ministers are serious about this target – and, if so, how can it be reached?

It was there in black and white in the party's manifesto, and has been repeated since the election by Tony Blair. Britain will cut its annual emissions of the main greenhouse gas to 80 per cent of its 1990 level over the next dozen years.

It remains to be seen if this target survives very long after the rest of the developed world signs up in Kyoto to far more modest cuts on Wednesday. But the fact is that Britain could do it, and lead the world in tackling climate change.

It would change the life of every family and the workings of most businesses over the next 10 years. Wind turbines would become as common as high-tension pylons.

We would have a cleaner country, since other kinds of pollution would reduce sharply, and a more efficient one. Our cities might be a little more densely packed, and our economy would continue to grow. In fact, it might make Britain rather more like Japan.

UK emissions have fallen by 5 per cent since 1990, due mainly to changes in the way we generate electricity. The proportion which comes from burning coal has fallen drastically. The share of burning natural gas, a fuel which produces less than half the carbon dioxide that coal does for each unit of electricity, has risen. So has that from nuclear power which produces virtually no carbon dioxide. But no new nuclear power stations are planned and its share will soon start falling. Emissions could be cut further if gas assumes a bigger share of electricity generation, but last week Mr Blair stepped on the brake to try to help the coal industry.

The trend is for emissions to rise with economic growth. As Britons get wealthier they want to fly more, drive more, buy more power-hungry gadgets. Without new policies, UK emissions will be 2 per cent higher in 2010 than in 1990, says the Energy Technology Support Unit (ETSU), the Government's leading energy advisers.

UK emissions have fallen by 5 per cent since 1990, due mainly to changes in the way we generate electricity

---

Falling gas and electricity bills are encouraging people to consume more energy. Only petrol and diesel prices are bucking the trend because the Government is committed to raising road fuel duties above the rate of inflation.

'The next steps are altogether more difficult,' said Dr Jim Skea, director of the Economic and Social Research Council's global environmental change programme. 'We need a transport, energy, fiscal and technology policy that reflects climate concerns.'

Most experts agree that to hit the target there would have to be higher household and industrial energy taxes – something the Government is loathe to contemplate. Some of the money those taxes raise will have to be re-directed into energy-saving incentives. Simply taxing fuel more 'has little chance of success', says Dr David Carless, of ETSU, 'and every chance of creating large areas of resentment'.

© *The Independent*
December, 1997

KenPyne

All that Kyoto heat, for next to nothing

After a night of agonising, last-minute negotiations, the world finally agreed a treaty to combat global warming today. It was being hailed as historic, but the long-sought agreement will do little to slow down the heating of the planet, as Nicholas Schoon and Richard Lloyd Parry report from Kyoto

After eleven days and three nights of some of the most complex international negotiations undertaken, the world's industrialised countries agreed on a legally-binding commitment to cut their annual emissions of climate-changing pollution by 5.2 per cent by 2012.

Europe will take the biggest cut – 8 per cent down from 1990 levels, but Britain's share is expected to be more. For the United States, the world's largest greenhouse gas emitter, the reduction is 7 per cent. Conference host Japan succeeded in negotiating itself a smaller cut, at 6 per cent.

An exhausted looking John Prescott, Britain's Deputy Prime Minister, said: 'It is a historic step but of course there is a lot more to do. It has been one heck of a process.'

But the compromises and hard bargaining involved in negotiating the new treaty, to be known as the Kyoto Protocol, disappointed environmentalists, vulnerable island nations, and were well short of the 15 per cent cut the European Union had long demanded for the developed world.

With many of the details of its implementation left for further talks, the Kyoto conference amounts to little more than an opening declaration of the war against global warming. Tony Juniper, campaigns director of Friends of the Earth, said: 'They've reached a political compromise here, but the climate remains as compromised as ever. The science shows that this agreement will not slow global warming.'

The fast-growing pollution from developing countries will outweigh the cuts which have now been agreed by the developing ones. That means the build-up of greenhouse gases will continue to accelerate. But the hope is that many Third World nations can be brought into the new treaty over the next few years.

Europe will take the biggest cut – 8 per cent down from 1990 levels, but Britain's share is expected to be more

---

The agreement, which also covers Russia and Eastern Europe, takes in the six most important greenhouse gases. For some countries the cut works out at less than 6 per cent, and others were able to plead special circumstances and win a small increase in legal emissions.

The conference overran its scheduled deadline by more than nine hours. At one point its chairman, Raul Estrada-Oyuela, called for a brief cooling-off period, saying: 'Perhaps we are going to blow up the whole possibility of an agreement.'

The US suffered a last-minute setback when an article in the treaty enabling developing countries to join the treaty by volunteering limits on their rising greenhouse gas emissions was thrown out because it could not find agreement.

The treaty will mark the birth of an entirely new global trading commodity – greenhouse gas allowance, which will be sold by countries with low emissions and bought by heavy polluters who wish to continue burning fossil fuels above their quota.

© *The Independent*
December, 1997

WWF's climate change campaign

The 1980s was the hottest decade in a century and the 1990s may turn out to be hotter still. As the world swelters and global weather patterns seem on the verge of spiralling out of control, scientists believe the climate is changing faster than at any time in the last 10,000 years.

The situation is so serious, and the threat to many of the world's most precious species and ecosystems so grave, that WWF has launched a major new campaign to try and halt climate change.

The greenhouse effect is real, and it's happening now. Scientists are certain that emissions of greenhouse gases from the burning of fossil fuels such as coal and oil are causing climate change. We need your help to persuade governments and industry to stop delaying and take the steps necessary to prevent a climate catastrophe.

WWF's campaign targets

- Reduction of CO_2 emissions by at least 20% from 1990 levels by developed countries by the year 2005.
- Promotion and widespread utilisation of energy-efficient technologies in China, India, and eastern Europe.
- Identification of the species and ecosystems most vulnerable to climate change and development of strategies for their conservation.

Our warming world

No part of the world will be immune to the menace of climate change, and in some places the effects can already be seen. The vast forests of Siberia and Canada are drying up, making them more susceptible to fires and attacks by insect pests. Glaciers are melting all across the world, and snow-mass is shrinking from the Andes to the Alps. Warmer sea temperatures seem to be behind the 'coral bleaching' that is seriously damaging reefs throughout the tropics. Scientists are in no doubt that the warming trend is the result of human activity polluting the atmosphere.

And the heat keeps rising. The summer of 1995 was one for the record books. Continuing a trend of summers hotter than any in the past 600 years, heatwaves swept across the northern hemisphere, with severe droughts taking hold in northern Europe. In the USA, the extreme heat killed hundreds of people and shrivelled maize crops. All of this was accompanied by the most severe hurricane season in the North Atlantic for more than 50 years.

Ecological limits

How much warming can nature tolerate before ecosystems begin to break down? Changes in the climate – the start and end of the Ice Age for instance – have occurred before and nature may have been able to adapt in many cases. But that was before humans appeared on the scene.

Now, with most of the world's remaining habitat broken into small patches and hemmed in on all sides by agriculture, roads, or urbanisation, wildlife will not have the chance to migrate away from the changing climate. In any case, many ecosystems are already so weakened by environmental degradation that they exhibit little capacity to cope with a new stress.

Wildlife including polar bear, walrus, golden toad, Kirtland's warbler, and brook trout may be threatened in large parts of their ranges. The most vulnerable habitats include coastal wetlands, tropical cloud forests, arctic tundra, and alpine flower meadows.

Species will become extinct as the climate warms, but we can minimise the losses if we act now.

Who is to blame?

The world's rapidly expanding human population continually adds to the build-up of greenhouse gases in the atmosphere. Since the Industrial Revolution, the concentration of CO_2 (the main greenhouse gas) in the air has risen by one-quarter, chiefly as a result of burning coal and oil. More than 90% of this CO_2 was produced by developed countries.

The only way to protect the world from global warming is to reduce greenhouse-gas emissions. WWF believes that the best way to do this is to change the way we use energy. People living in industrialised countries need to use it more efficiently, and switch to cleaner sources of energy such as wind and solar power. Elsewhere, countries should be helped to develop energy programmes based on those cleaner sources. The solutions become more complex and costly the longer we wait.

Although world-wide policy changes are required, small actions can help. For instance, one way individuals can help is by switching to energy-efficient light bulbs. It really works: since 1987, sales in these light bulbs have jumped tenfold, saving the equivalent energy output of nearly 40 coal-fired power stations.

What is WWF doing?

Promoting energy efficiency
WWF is helping support six energy-efficiency centres in China, Russia, and eastern Europe. The local energy experts that staff and run these centres have achieved some remarkable successes. In China, recommendations from the WWF-sponsored centre resulted in the cancellation of a proposed coal-fired power station. The Russian centre drafted standards for energy efficiency that have been formally adopted by Moscow's City Council. In Poland, an energy education centre has been inaugurated and a series of TV programmes promoting energy efficiency produced.

Strengthening the Climate Convention
At the 1992 Earth Summit in Rio de Janeiro, 153 nations signed the Climate Convention in recognition of the urgent need to combat global warming. Industrialised countries agreed to return their greenhouse-gas emissions to 1990 levels by the year 2000. This target is too weak to prevent rapid climatic change, and few countries are on track to achieve even this meagre aim. WWF is working to make the convention more effective and to ensure that industralised nations commit themselves to at least a 20% cut in 1990 CO_2 emissions by 2005.

Assessing wildlife impacts
In 1987, WWF was the first organisation to alert the world to the threat climate change poses to species and habitat. Remaining at the cutting edge of research and policy in this field, WWF has published a series of reports detailing the potential losses to natural ecosystems. The organisation assisted the US government by developing a computer programme for determining the impacts of climate on wildlife populations, and worked with local scientists to review climate threats in China and southern Africa. WWF also recently published the first scientific studies demonstrating that tropical forests will be seriously affected by changes in rainfall patterns caused by the greenhouse effect.

© WWF
January, 1998

The world in 2050

According to the UN's international panel of 2,500 scientists, these are some of the disasters facing the Earth if current trends continue

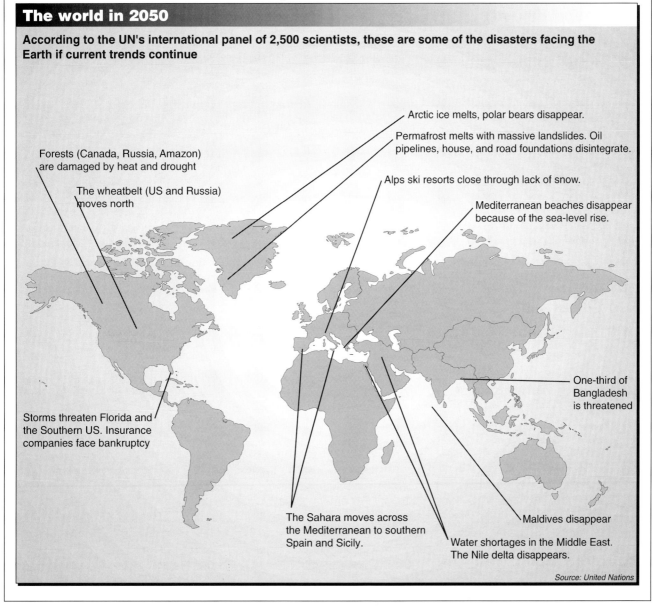

Arctic ice melts, polar bears disappear.

Permafrost melts with massive landslides. Oil pipelines, house, and road foundations disintegrate.

Forests (Canada, Russia, Amazon) are damaged by heat and drought

Alps ski resorts close through lack of snow.

The wheatbelt (US and Russia) moves north

Mediterranean beaches disappear because of the sea-level rise.

One-third of Bangladesh is threatened

Storms threaten Florida and the Southern US. Insurance companies face bankruptcy

The Sahara moves across the Mediterranean to southern Spain and Sicily.

Maldives disappear

Water shortages in the Middle East. The Nile delta disappears.

Source: United Nations

The DIY guide to combating global warming

The time to act is now

At long last governments are beginning to realise the true enormity of the threat of global warming. Through the work of the United Nations Environment Programme, they are slowly moving towards international agreement to limit global warming and reduce its impact.

The immediate priorities must be:

- to use less energy, as most energy is produced by burning coal, gas or oil
- to reduce dependence on fossil fuels by switching to other sources of energy which do less harm to the environment
- to protect the world's remaining forests and to encourage reforestation
- to eliminate production and use of the chlorofluorocarbons and related chemicals
- to find ways of reducing agricultural emissions

But this process will take time – international protocols must be agreed upon, legislation must be devised, laws must be passed and measures must be implemented. It could be ten or fifteen years before we see any substantial result.

But, as individuals, we don't have to wait. We are free to act now and our actions will have an immediate effect. We can reduce the threat of global warming and, as we do so, create an atmosphere in which our politicians will move faster and more effectively, motivated and supported by public pressure and opinion.

While the primary responsibility for dealing with the greenhouse problem must rest with government, commerce and industry, we all have a role to play.

This article provides a starting-point.

In the home

One-sixth of the energy produced world-wide is used in the home – more than the Middle Eastern oil nations produce every year. Consumption of electricity and gas creates a significant proportion of greenhouse pollution. Much of this use is unnecessary.

Around three-quarters of the energy used in the typical British home is devoted to water and space heating, like central heating – about a third of this is wasted due to poor insulation.

Energy-efficient light bulbs are on the market that offer electricity savings of up to eighty per cent, and a lifetime five times as long as traditional bulbs. If you lower your thermostat by just one degree, the amount of energy you use – and your heating bill – could be reduced by almost ten per cent.

There are many ways in which we can be more energy-efficient in the home and thereby reduce the greenhouse effect.

But it's not just a question of energy use. Almost every household uses products which contain chlorofluorocarbons, CFCs. These gases are still found in some aerosol cans and all refrigerators use CFCs in their cooling systems and for insulation.

Walk round your house and identify the ways in which you are contributing to the greenhouse problem. The following points represent a few first steps you can take to limit global warming.

1. If you are buying a flat or house, check its energy efficiency.

Find out how energy-efficient your future home is by undertaking a home energy audit (contact the Energy Efficiency Office for more details) or by asking your surveyor to check the extent of loft insulation and other energy-saving measures. If possible, ask to see past electricity and gas bills.

2. If you are a council tenant, ask your local authority for an energy audit.

Council property should be designed for maximum energy conservation. An energy audit will reveal whether or not this is the case. Both you and the council will benefit from energy savings. If such measures were standard, heating bills would be reduced and there would be less default on rents – inability to pay for heating is a major cause.

3. Insulate your home.

You can gain a lot by properly insulating lofts, walls, windows, doors, water pipes, hot water tanks and floors. Did you know that if our homes were insulated to Danish standards, carbon dioxide emissions would be reduced by over half a million tonnes a year? Lagging a hot-water tank with a thick jacket can reduce heat loss by three-quarters, covering the initial outlay in just weeks. About half the houses in the United Kingdom have cavity walls. Insulating these walls can halve heat loss. There are a number of different materials used in cavity wall insulation. Do be sure to avoid urea formaldehyde (UF) and polystyrene because of the toxins and CFCs they contain.

4. Insulate windows and doors and think about double glazing.

Draughts through windows and doors can account for as much as fifteen per cent of the total heat loss in a typical home. Single-glazed windows alone are responsible for up to a quarter of the heat lost. Double-glazing can halve this loss. Double-glazing with low-emissivity glass can halve it again! There are other benefits, too – double glazing reduces both condensation and external noise. Do make sure you use a reputable firm, though, and that you still have good ventilation.

5. Keep heating to a minimum.
If possible, have thermostats fitted to all your radiators – or make sure that the radiators are off in rooms you don't use. Check all your thermostats for maximum sensitivity, and replace them if necessary. You can also fit a thermostat to your hot water cylinder. Keep it at 120°F or 50°C.

6. If you have central heating, use a time switch.
A lot of energy can be saved by making sure heating is off when the house is empty. If you work away from home, make sure that your heating comes on only in the mornings and evenings. Remember, too, that your heating system will work best when regularly serviced.

7. Whenever possible, use cold water rather than hot.
Try using cold water to rinse dishes and floors – you'll save a lot of energy! Do not do the washing until you have a full load and use economy/cool settings. If you have very dirty laundry, try presoaking it rather than washing it twice or using a very hot setting.

8. Avoid using automatic dryers and limit ironing to necessities.
Hang clothes outside whenever you can rather than tumble drying. If you need to iron, plan your ironing sessions: start with cooler settings, working up to the hotter ones to save energy.

9. Don't buy unnecessary electric appliances.
Dishwashers, electric carving knives, hairdryers, electric coffee machines, electric mixers and so on are rarely essential. Think hard before you buy. A typical dishwasher uses as much as fourteen gallons of hot water a load. And are they really labour-saving? Many household jobs can be done as efficiently if hands are used!

10. Buy the most energy-efficient appliances available.
If your local dealer cannot advise you as to the most energy-efficient washing machine, freezer or fridge, tell them they should be able to! Consumer guides such as *Which?* Can be invaluable here – so research before you go shopping. Gas cookers

can use as little as a third the amount of energy used by electric cookers. Check which refrigerator manufacturers have reduced the CRC content in their appliance. One manufacturer, for example, produces a frost-free fridge-freezer which contains half the CRCs found in traditional lines. Washing machines are available which are weight-sensitive. They select the right amount of water for the weight of clothes in the load.

11. Substitute energy-efficient lighting for traditional bulbs.
These are more expensive initially, but the total cost of energy-efficient lighting is about half that of traditional lighting. Not only do energy-efficient bulbs consume a fraction of the electricity – they last five times longer. Simply changing one traditional bulb for an energy-efficient one can keep half a tonne of carbon dioxide out of the air.

12. Reduce lighting and heating levels and switch off what you're not using.
Beware of wasted energy. Turn off lights when you are not using a room – and train your children and visitors to do the same! Reduce overall lighting by using desk or side lamps rather than overhead lighting. Fit dimmer switches and replace existing bulbs with lower wattage ones if possible. Turn the thermostat on your heating system down – at least 1° – and wear a sweater. Don't leave appliances on – even on stand-by – when they are not in use.

13. Whatever your appliance, maximise its efficiency.
Use a kettle rather than a pan to boil water and only boil the amount of water you need. Descale kettles regularly – they'll work more efficiently. Put lids on pans when

cooking. Avoid keeping your fridge too cold and remember to defrost it regularly. Do not use a larger fridge-freezer than you need. For maximum efficiency, keep your freezer section three-quarters full and stuff empty spaces with newspaper.

14. Learn more about saving energy.
Electricity and gas showrooms should be good sources of information on home energy conservation, stocking pamphlets containing practical ideas for saving energy and money. If they're not, ask why not. The more people ask for information, the more likely they are to respond to demand!

For further information

- Energy Efficiency Office, Distribution Unit, Department of Energy, 1 Palace Street, London SW1 (ask for their literature on energy conservation in the home).

- ECSC, 99 Midland Road, London NW12 2AH – produce the *Heating Advice Handbook*, published by the London Energy and Employment Network.

- National Cavity Wall Insulation Association Ltd, External Wall Insulation Association, Draught Proofing Advisory Association Ltd, National Association of Loft Insulation Contractors, c/o Corporate Public Relations Ltd, PO Box 12, Haslemere, Surrey GU27 3AN.

- The Solar Trade Association, Brackenhurst, Greenham Common South, Newbury RG15 8HH – can provide literature on the domestic applications of solar power.

- Consumers Association, 14 Buckingham Street, London WC2N 6DS – publishers of *Which?* Magazine – can help you identify energy-efficient appliances and products.

- Energy and Environment Unit, Scottish Development Agency, 120 Bothwell Street, Glasgow G2 7JP

Please be sure to enclose a SAE, preferably A4, when writing to these organisations.

Recycling

The United Kingdom dumps around thirty million tonnes of solid waste each year. This is a potential source of energy which, replacing fossil fuels, could produce heat and power for two and a half million homes, factories, schools or hospitals.

Yet ninety per cent of this waste is discarded – disposed of as landfill where it generates the greenhouse gas methane and other environmental hazards.

And much of the waste could be recycled. This would not only save energy, with less raw material having to be processed, but it would also conserve valuable resources such as the world's forests.

The problem is that recycling facilities are limited. For example, there aren't enough processing plants to handle the paper that is already being recycled. This would change if we were all to use recycled paper as much as possible, increasing demand so that more processing plants are built. We also need to lobby government and industry to support and subsidise improved recycling facilities.

You can make a valuable contribution by taking the following steps to reduce the waste endemic in our society.

15. Find out what recycling facilities there are in your area,

Local councils are responsible for the collection and disposal of refuse. This should extend to recycling. Urge your local council to collect recyclable waste separately or to set up collection points. Some councils have a recycling officer. If your local council does not have an officer then petition for one.

16. Separate your waste into recyclable and non-recyclable items.

There are five basic groups of recyclable waste – newspaper and magazines, other paper, glass, aluminium and organic waste. Once you know where the collection points are, you can take your recyclable wastes there rather than throwing them out with the rest of your rubbish. Set yourself the goal of reducing the contents of your dustbin by half!

17. Avoid products which can't be recycled.

Articles made of plastic cannot be recycled successfully in bulk as there are so many different types of plastic.

Avoid buying them if possible. If the item you need is only available in plastic containers, write to the store manager or, better still, the manufacturer asking why they don't provide recycling facilities. You could suggest they convert to a type of container that can be reused.

18. Encourage everyone you know to recycle and support local recycling initiatives.

The average household throws away around six trees' worth of paper every year. If this was recycled and used to make more paper, it would reduce the demand for wood pulp – and save an awful lot of trees. Voluntary groups can often boost their income by holding paper and aluminium collections. If you're a member of such a group, bring it up at the next meeting.

19. Lobby local branches of fast-food chains about environmentally-sound, recyclable packaging.

Paper, aluminium and glass can be recycled – most plastic and foam packaging cannot. The packaging of many fast-food chains is manufactured using CFCs – potent greenhouse gases.

20. Recycle or reuse as many household goods as possible.

Old cottons – sheets, pillowcases and towels, for instance – can be used as floor cloths, dusters, and so on. Charities such as Oxfam or the Salvation Army will take clothing, appliances and furniture, as will many community groups when holding jumble sales. Give worn-out electrical appliances to your local repair shop so that parts can be recycled.

21. Dispose of wastes safely.

This will protect both the environment and your health. Waste motor oil will be taken by most garages – if yours doesn't then ask if they could provide this facility. It is possible to recover the CRCs in old refrigerators so that they don't pollute

the atmosphere. One major freezer food chain will dispose of old fridges, as will some local councils. Ask your local council to provide information about the safe disposal of hazardous waste.

22. If you have a garden, start a compost heap.

All your organic refuse can be converted to valuable compost. If you haven't a garden, a neighbour may appreciate it!

23. Use recycled paper products whenever possible.

Millions of trees are cut down every year to satisfy our demand for paper. Recycled paper of all qualities is now being produced – some suppliers are listed at the end. If the demand for this rises, then recycling schemes will become more effective as waste paper fetches higher prices. Do avoid recycled paper which has been heavily bleached using chlorine as, in most cases, this releases dioxins – a carcinogen – into the environment.

24. Return junk mail in prepaid envelopes.

Junk mail kills trees. So make use of those prepaid envelopes – return them to the sender without filling in your name and address but with a note objecting strongly to the waste of paper.

For further information

- FoE/Daily Telegraph Recycling Guides – an invaluable starting-point. Available from local W H Smiths, Sainsbury's and some Esso garages, these will give details of recycling facilities in your area.
- Friends of the Earth, Recycling Department, 26-28 Underwood Street, London N1 7JQ – for further information on recycling.
- Aluminium Can Recycling Association. For free information pack, telephone 0800 444222, or write to: CV1037 Conrad House, Birmingham Road, Stratford-upon-Avon CV37 0AZ.
- British Glass, Northumberland Road, Sheffield S10 2UA – for advice on bottle banks.
- British Paper and Board Industry Federation, Papermakers House, Rivenhall Rd, Westlea, Swindon SN5 7BE – should be able to provide information on manu-

facturers and stockists of recycled paper and board.

- British Plastics Federation, 5 Belgrave Square, London SW1X 8PD.
- British Scrap Federation, 16 High Street, Brampton, Huntingdon PE18 8TU.
- The Warmer Campaign, 83 Mount Ephraim, Tunbridge Wells, Kent TN4 8BR – for advice on separating waste.
- Waste Watch, 26 Bedford Square, London WC1B 3HU – for advice on separating waste.

Some suppliers of recycled papers

- Forestsaver, Freepost, PO Box 1, Portishead BS20 9BR
- Traidcraft PLC, Kingsway, Gateshead, Tyne and Wear NE11 0NE
- Paperback, Bow Triangle Business Centre, Unit 2, Eleanor Street, London E3 4NP.
- Conservation Papers, 228 London Road, Reading, Berkshire RG6 1AH.
- Earthwrite Cooperative Ltd, Unit 1B, Carlisle House, Carlisle Street East, Sheffield S4 7QN.

Please be sure to enclose a SAE, preferably A4, when writing to these organisations.

Saving water

Fresh water is the most valuable resource on the planet. It is, quite literally, the source of life – without it, humans, plants and animals would not be able to survive. Yet it's a resource that we take very much for granted; turn on the tap – and there it is. Some of us were brought face to face with our dependence on water during the long, hot summer of 1989. Many areas were subjected to hose-pipe bans, some had to collect water from standpipes in the streets as reserves became more and more depleted. There is an important lesson to be learnt from this experience.

As climate changes, rainfall patterns will alter and, in some areas, water supplies may well become depleted. It is not possible at the moment to say exactly how or where the change will come, but it is important to be prepared and to look

carefully at our use of water so that we eliminate waste as much as possible. We need to begin changing our water-use habits now.

As well as eliminating waste, we must also ensure that water pollution is tackled effectively. This will protect both our health and the environment at large. A degraded environment is much more susceptible to the consequences of climate change than a healthy one.

The following steps are practical ways in which you can help protect our precious water resources. Once you have decided to implement them, you will find that they become habit – just a part of your normal routine.

25. Take a shower rather than a bath.
A five-minute shower consumes approximately fifteen gallons of water, half the amount of water – and energy – that a full bath takes. And five minutes is a long time in the shower!

26. Repair all leaks and drips immediately.
Often, all that a dripping tap needs is the washer replaced – yet this simple step can stop up to two gallons of water leaking away each day.

27. Use a water filter.
Until such time as the quality of tap water improves, you may like to use a filter, either fitted to the cold water supply in your kitchen or by investing in one of the jugs that are now readily available. These will remove – in varying degrees depending on the type – pollutants such as heavy metals and nitrates.

28. Consider having a low-flush toilet installed.
These have a choice of two flushes – a long or a short – and this greatly reduces the amount of water used. If you cannot have one of these installed, try putting a brick in the cistern to reduce the amount of water in each flush.

29. Re-use household water.
Try using bath water to water the garden – or for the first soak of very dirty clothes.

30. Make the most of rainy days by collecting rain water.
Rain water is usually softer than tap water. It is good for washing hair and for watering plants. Keep your

container covered when it's not raining to keep bugs, leaves – and pets – out!

31. Eat less meat.
It takes one hundred times as much water to produce a pound of meat as it does to grow a pound of wheat.

32. Don't contribute to water pollution.
Use phosphate-free washing powder and avoid chlorine bleaches. Check loo cleaners and household products for ingredients which might damage water organisms. If you're not sure what it is or what it does – avoid it!

33. Ensure that your water authority is treating sewage fully.
About one in five sewage treatment works in England and Wales are breaking laws by discharging effluents that fail to meet quality standards. Find out if this is happening in your area – and, if it is, write and complain.

34. If you have doubts about the quality of your tap water, ask your local water supplier to analyse it.
Water authorities are legally obliged to state when levels of contaminants in tap water breach European Community limits. By reporting all such infringements, you can encourage prosecution of offenders and force an improvement in the quality of your tap water.

For registering complaints about tap water quality

- Commission of the European Communities, Rue de la Roi 200, B-1049 Bruxelles, Belgium.
- UK Press and Information Office of the European Communities, 8 Storey's Gate, London SW1 3AT.
- National Rivers Authority, 30-34 Albert Embankment, London SE1 7TL.
- Your local water supplier – see your local telephone directory.

Friends of the Earth (26-28 Underwood Street, London N1 7JQ) can provide complaints forms. Please be sure to include a SAE, preferably A4

- The above is an extract from *The DIY guide to combating global warming – 101 hot tips to cool the earth*, produced by ARK. See page 41 for address details.

© Ark Campaigns Ltd

The future of the climate

Reacting, adapting and mitigating

If, as the Intergovernmental Panel on Climate Change (IPPC) suggests, the enhanced greenhouse effect is likely to cause warming in the first century of the new millennium, what should we do? The IPCC itself summarised the options:

- implementing low-cost measures, such as energy efficiency, to reduce emissions of greenhouse gases;
- phasing out existing distortionary policies, such as some fossil-fuel subsidies, that reduce welfare and increase greenhouse-gas emissions directly or indirectly;
- switching from more to less carbon-intensive fuels or to carbon-free fuels to reduce emissions of greenhouse gases;
- enhancing or expanding greenhouse gas sinks or reservoirs, such as forests;
- implementing existing techniques (and developing new ones) for reducing methane and nitrous oxide emissions from industrial processes, landfills, agriculture, fossil-fuel extraction and transportation;
- instituting forms of international co-operation, such as joint implementation, technology transfer and tradable quotas to reduce the cost of limiting greenhouse gas emissions;
- planning and implementing measures to adapt to the consequences of climate change;
- undertaking additional research on climate-change causes, effects and adaptation (economic studies suggest that such research can yield high returns by reducing uncertainty about actions to address climate change);
- conducting technological research to enhance energy efficiency, minimise emissions of greenhouse gases from fossil-fuel use, and develop commercial non-fossil energy sources (in the long run, the cost and timing of availability of non-fossil energy technologies is one of the major determinants of the cost of addressing climate change);
- developing institutional mechanisms, such as insurance, to share the risks of damages due to climate change.

One area of considerable debate, however, has been how and when we should adapt to global warming. It is often said that there are two types of adaptation that may be necessary. The first of these types is reactive adaptation, whereby we adopt a wait-and-see attitude and respond to climatic change after it occurs. Alternatively, there is anticipatory adaptation, in which we take steps in advance of anticipated climate changes to minimise any potentially negative effects or to increase our ability to adapt to changes rapidly and inexpensively. In other words we hedge our bets.

Reactive adaptation may well be both feasible and effective. In many parts of the world we may find it possible to adapt to the most likely scenarios of future climatic change. We could, for instance, substitute heat- and drought-resistant crop varieties for those whose yields are

reduced. Likewise, infrastructure, which is generally replaced on a much faster timescale than climatic change, could be modified to cope with changes in climate. It can also be argued that reactive adaptation is a strategy that does not involve spending money prematurely before some hypothetical changes occur.

On the other hand one can argue that a rapid climate change or significant increases in the frequency and intensity of extreme hazards such as floods, storms or droughts could make reactive adaptations more difficult and could create a threat for large numbers of people. Equally, some policies would have significant and tangible benefits even under current environmental conditions and would be valuable from a benefit/cost point of view even if no climatic change were to take place.

These types of anticipatory policies are often called 'no-regrets policies' because they will succeed whether or not climatic change takes place, meaning that policy-makers should never have to regret their adoption. No-regrets policies may, nonetheless, be expensive, but we may get what is called a 'double benefit'. Thus if we slow the rate of deforestation in the humid tropics to decrease the rate of CO_2 emissions from biomass burning, we are also helping to preserve biodiversity. If we reduce CO_2 emissions through energy efficiency and conservation, we reduce other pollutants (for example, sulphur dioxide). If we succeed in reducing carbon dioxide emissions from traffic the policies that are likely to be used also reduce local pollution, noise, accidents and congestion. One could also, perhaps at no great cost, introduce planning controls to limit development in sensitive locations, such as highly populated, low-lying coastal plains.

A cogent reason that is given for taking action now, in spite of all the uncertainties, is that the time-scale of atmospheric response is long. CO_2 that is being emitted into the atmosphere now will contribute to the increased concentration of this gas and the associated climate change for over a hundred years. Hence the more CO_2 that is emitted now, the more difficult it will prove to reduce the levels to those that will eventually be required. Moreover, the timescales for certain human responses can be long, as illustrated by the fact that the power stations that will produce our electric power three or four decades hence are being planned and built today.

According to what is called the Precautionary Principle we need to take out what is in effect an insurance policy against surprises and the unexpected. Even though the risk posed by such possibilities is impossible to assess and cannot therefore easily be quantified, it would not perhaps be prudent to ignore entirely unexpected possibilities in weighing the action that may be necessary.

It is also important for policy-makers to have a clear view of the costs and benefits of global warming, for it is plainly crucial in determining whether it is worth spending large amounts of money to combat this potential threat. Environmental economists have been addressing this issue with vigour for some years. There are extreme difficulties in placing a value on such issues as biodiversity and amenity. Nonetheless some quantification of the costs of action against the likely costs of the consequences of inaction should at least be attempted.

The key need, if action is to be taken and to be effective, is to reduce emissions of greenhouse-enhancing gases. There are various means by which this might be achieved. First of all, it is possible to conserve energy and to use it more efficiently, by such means as insulating houses, designing domestic appliances that use less power and increasing the efficiency of coal-fired power stations and developing combined heat and power schemes. Likewise it is

necessary to look at alternative means of power generation, including efficient gas-powered stations, nuclear stations and various types of renewable energy sources powered by sun, wind, water or biomass.

Some scientists have argued that the world's forests can make a contribution to the mitigation of global warming, either by reducing the rates of deforestation (especially in the tropics) or by active afforestation. Both processes would help to store carbon rather than releasing it into the atmosphere. Similarly, methane emissions could be minimised by reducing biomass burning associated with defores-tation, by recycling waste or using gas generated from waste for energy production, and by reducing leakage from natural gas pipelines.

Another method that has been proposed to control CO_2 emissions is a system of 'joint implementation schemes', 'carbon offsets' or 'tradable emissions permits'. The idea behind this is that countries which find they have high abatement costs could be credited for cheaper abatement efforts undertaken in other countries. For example, an industrialised

country might choose to plant forests (and so sequestrate carbon) in a developing country.

One can also ask whether we have a clear picture, if we wish to apportion blame and charge the polluter, about national carbon dioxide inventories. Do we charge polluters for their past emissions or their present emissions? Should we tax an Asian peasant whose buffalo and paddy field emit methane in the way we might tax a California adolescent who owns a large dune buggy that emits carbon dioxide?

Since the Industrial Revolution, industrialised countries have 'used up' more than their fair share of the atmospheric resource, causing cumulative pollution. In other words it can be argued that industrialised countries have already incurred a large debt and should accordingly be allowed smaller future emission levels. They have become richer in part because they have used up a disproportionate amount of the atmospheric resource and should thus compensate the poor by allowing them larger future emission levels. On the other hand, should the 'sins' of fathers be visited on their sons?

The concept of introducing a carbon tax to reduce CO_2 emissions, although seemingly simple, has not been universally welcomed. It has been argued that unless the tax were large it would be ineffective but that if it were large it would be politically unacceptable. Moreover, since a carbon tax is unlikely to be introduced by all countries, energy-intense industries might switch to those countries which did not introduce a tax. Indeed, given that many European countries are already very energy efficient, it is conceivable that any shift of production to less energy-efficient parts of the world could actually raise rather than depress global CO_2 emissions. This effect is sometimes called 'carbon leakage'.

There are also various problems with the costs of strategies to reduce emissions. It is agreed that any draconian measures could retard economic development. Moreover, the countries that can afford to combat greenhouse warming will not be the main beneficiaries of abatement policies. It is those countries potentially most at risk from the effects of global warming and sea-level rise, such as Bangladesh, that can least afford to divert resources from their own development. It is a moot question whether the world's greatest producer of carbon-dioxide emissions, the United States of America, would wish to spend money now to benefit other countries that might suffer from global warming in the future.

Linked with this is the question of whether the developed countries that have achieved a high level of economic development through the lavish use of fossil-fuel resources could expect the less developed and poor nations of the world to limit their use of fossil fuels and their rate of economic advancement. Similarly, can countries that have already cut down most of their own forests, such as Britain, argue with any great authority that developing countries should not follow their example?

So, then, there are controversies about whether anticipatory adaptation is desirable in itself and about the feasibility of the various methods that might be employed were it to prove acceptable. If the majority of governments in the world (and individuals) take anticipatory adaptation seriously, there is some prospect that rates of global warming could at least be slowed down. It is, however, by no means certain that this will prove to be the case. A combination of prevailing short-termism, cheerful optimism and climatological cynicism may defeat the efforts of those who see the wisdom of no-regrets policies.

• The above is an extract from *The Future of the Climate* (ISBN 0 297 81929 1) by Andrew Goudie, Professor of Geography at the University of Oxford. *The Future of the Climate* is one title within a series called *Predictions* published by Phoenix, priced at £2.00.

© *The Future of Climate*, *Andrew Goudie 1997*

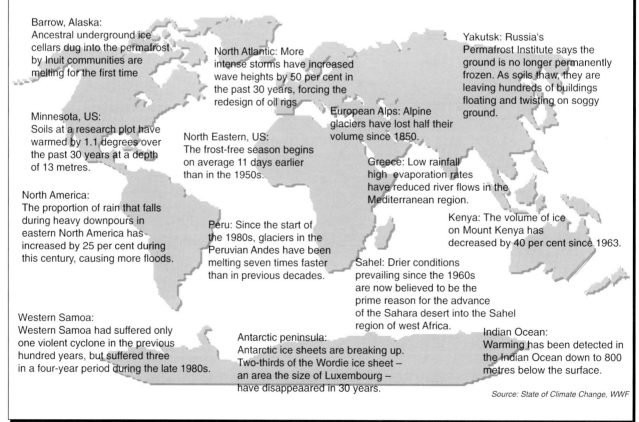

A global inventory of first physical impacts of climate change

Melting ice caps, warming oceans, droughts and expanding deserts – all evidence of the present impacts of global warming on the ecoregions of the earth.

Barrow, Alaska: Ancestral underground ice cellars dug into the permafrost by Inuit communities are melting for the first time

North Atlantic: More intense storms have increased wave heights by 50 per cent in the past 30 years, forcing the redesign of oil rigs

Yakutsk: Russia's Permafrost Institute says the ground is no longer permanently frozen. As soils thaw, they are leaving hundreds of buildings floating and twisting on soggy ground.

Minnesota, US: Soils at a research plot have warmed by 1.1 degrees over the past 30 years at a depth of 13 metres.

North Eastern, US: The frost-free season begins on average 11 days earlier than in the 1950s.

European Alps: Alpine glaciers have lost half their volume since 1850.

North America: The proportion of rain that falls during heavy downpours in eastern North America has increased by 25 per cent during this century, causing more floods.

Greece: Low rainfall high evaporation rates have reduced river flows in the Mediterranean region.

Peru: Since the start of the 1980s, glaciers in the Peruvian Andes have been melting seven times faster than in previous decades.

Kenya: The volume of ice on Mount Kenya has decreased by 40 per cent since 1963.

Sahel: Drier conditions prevailing since the 1960s are now believed to be the prime reason for the advance of the Sahara desert into the Sahel region of west Africa.

Western Samoa: Western Samoa had suffered only one violent cyclone in the previous hundred years, but suffered three in a four-year period during the late 1980s.

Antarctic peninsula: Antarctic ice sheets are breaking up. Two-thirds of the Wordie ice sheet – an area the size of Luxembourg – have disappeaared in 30 years.

Indian Ocean: Warming has been detected in the Indian Ocean down to 800 metres below the surface.

Source: State of Climate Change, WWF

ADDITIONAL RESOURCES

You might like to contact the following organisations for further information. Due to the increasing cost of postage, many organisations cannot respond to enquiries unless they receive a stamped, addressed envelope.

Atmospheric Research & Information Centre
Manchester Metropolitan University
Chester Street
Manchester, M1 5GD
Tel: 0161 247 1590
Fax: 0161 247 6332
Runs education and information programmes for air quality, acid rain and global climate change. They produce a wide range of leaflets and information packs.

Climate Action Network (CAN – UK)
c/o Media Natura
21 Tower Street
London, WC2H 9NS
Tel: 0171 836 1110
Fax: 0171 497 0447
Works on climate change issues in the UK. Organises major conferences, produces reports, newsletters and factsheets.

Countryside Commission
Environmental Protection Unit
John Dower House
Crescent Place
Cheltenham
Gloucestershire, GL50 3RA
Tel: 01242 521 381
Fax: 01242 584 270
Works to protect and enhance the countryside for the general public. Produces many publications.

Department of the Environment
Global Atmosphere Division
Romney House
43 Marsham Street
London, SW1P 3PY
Tel: 0171 276 3000
Fax: 0171 890 5269
Produces publications including *Climate Change*.

Friends of the Earth
26-28 Underwood Street
London, N1 7JQ
Tel: 0171 490 1555
Fax: 0171 490 0881
Web site: See page 43 for details
As an independent environmental group, Friends of the Earth publishes a comprehensive range of leaflets, books and in-depth briefings and reports.

Greenpeace
Canonbury Villas
London, N1 2PN
Tel: 0171 865 8100
Fax: 0171 865 8200
Web site: See page 43 for details
Protects the environment through peaceful direct action. Actions on land and sea against whaling, nuclear power, air and water pollution and the exploitation of wildlife.

National Society for Clean Air and Environmental Protection (NSCA)
136 North Street
Brighton
East Sussex, BN1 1RG
Tel: 01273 326313
Tel: 01273 735802
Works towards environmental improvement by promoting clean air through the reduction of pollution, noise and other contaminants. Produces leaflets, journals, conference papers, factsheets, booklets and teaching packs (including a photocopiable teacher's pack: Global Warming).

Natural Environment Research Council
Polaris House, North Star Avenue
Swindon
Wiltshire, SN2 1EU
Tel: 01793 411500
Fax: 01793 411501
Provides specialist scientific facilities and services to meet the needs of UK environmental sciences. Produces publications.

The Ark Environmental Foundation
Suite 640-643, Linen Hall
162-168 Regent Street
London, W1R 5TB
Tel: 0171 439 4567
Ark believes that the wants of consumers and the needs of the environment are not necessarily incompatible. Produces publications.

United Nations Environmental Programme (UNEP)
Information Unit on Climate Change
C.P. 356
1219 Châtelaine
Geneva
Switzerland
Tel: 00 41 22 9799242
Fax: 00 41 22 797 3464
Web site: See page 43 for details
Publishes free material including *Climate Change* – a comprehensive loose leaf information kit (published November, 1997).

World Wide Fund For Nature (WWF-UK)
Panda House
Weyside Park
Catteshall Lane
Godalming, GU7 1XR
Tel: 01483 426444
Fax: 01483 426409
Promotes the wise use of the world's natural resources. Produces a wide range of factsheets and other publications. Ask for their publications list.

Young People's Trust for the Environment and Nature Conservation (YPTENC)
8 Leapale Road
Guildford, GU2 4PG
Tel: 01483 539600
Fax: 01483 301992
Works to educate young people in matters relating to the conservation of the world's wild places and natural resources. Produces publications.

INDEX

acid rain 17, 22
agriculture
    and climate change 5, 6, 19
    impact of set-aside 17
air pollution 13, 17, 18
Alaska 22, 23, 28, 40
Antarctica 5, 21, 22, 40
Arctic
    Alaska 22, 23, 28, 40
    icebergs as water resource 15
    thawing ice 5, 22-3, 33
asthma 18
Atlantic Conveyor Belt 6
Australia
    droughts 23
    and greenhouse gas emissions 20

beaches, shrinking 18, 19
birds 21, 26

carbon dioxide (CO2)
    and algae 9
    atmospheric levels 4
      and global warming 9
    emissions 1, 6, 27
      effects on vegetation 3
      reducing 14, 25, 27, 28, 32-3, 38-40
      stabilizing 2, 6
    UK 30
    and the greenhouse effect 24
    and plant growth 5
carbon taxes 39-40
CFCs (chlorofluorocarbons) 24, 25, 34, 36
cholera, and global warming 13
cliffs, erosion of 16
Climate Change Convention (1992) 2, 33
clouds 5,6
coral bleaching 23, 32
countryside, UK 10-11, 16-18

deforestation 6, 24, 25, 27, 32
desertification 5, 19
developing countries, and greenhouse gas emissions 31, 40
diseases, and global warming 13, 15, 19
droughts 25
    and El Niño 23, 28
    in the UK 11, 12, 16

Earth Summit, Climate Change Convention (1992) 2, 33
ecosystems 10-11, 32
El Niños 6, 23
    economic effects of 27-8
environmental effects of climate change 1, 3
Europe
    effects of climate change 14
    greenhouse gas emission reductions 31
    tropical illnesses in 13

flooding 1, 3, 5, 25, 26
food supplies, and climate change 1, 3, 14, 19
forestry
    and climate change in the UK 11, 14, 17
    deforestation 6, 24, 25, 27, 32
fossil fuel burning 1, 6, 9, 24, 25

glaciers, melting of 5, 19, 22, 23, 32, 40
global warming
    causes 24
    costs and benefits of 39
    effects 24-5
    rise in global temperatures 1, 3, 4-5, 6, 9, 19, 24-5, 32
    uncertainties over 5-6
greenhouse gases 24
    atmospheric levels 4
    and climate change 2
    emissions
      reducing 20, 27, 29, 30, 31, 32-3, 38-40
      stabilizing 2, 6
    environmental effects of 1, 3
    and global temperature rises 1, 3, 4-5, 6
    rising levels 1

ice cover 6
    thawing of 5, 22-3, 33

Japan
    greenhouse gas emission reductions 28, 29, 31
    Kyoto Climate Summit (1997) 2, 19, 20, 28, 29, 30, 31

malaria, and global warming 13, 15, 19
methane
    atmospheric levels 4, 6
    emissions 1, 6, 24
      reducing 38, 39

nitrous oxide
    atmospheric levels 4
    emissions 1, 24
      reducing 38

oceans
    sea temperature rises 6, 16, 18, 40
    tropical 23
ozone pollution 1
    and the countryside 17, 18

Pacific Islands, global warming 20
penguins 21, 22

rainfall 40
    in Britain 14, 16
      and agriculture 17
    in the tropics 23
recreation, and climate change in the UK 12, 17-18

sea temperature rises 6, 16, 18, 40
sea-level rises 1, 3, 5, 19
    in the Pacific Islands 20

Independence Web News

[Back] [Forward] [Home] | [Reload] [Images] [Open] [Print] [Find] | [Stop]

[Live Home Page] [Net Search] [Apple Computer] [Apple Support] [Apple Software]

The Internet has been likened to shopping in a supermarket without aisles. The press of a button on a Web browser can bring up thousands of sites but working your way though them to find what you want can involve long and frustrating on-line searches. And unfortunately many sites contain inaccurate, misleading or heavily biased information. Our researchers have therefore undertaken an extensive analysis to bring you a selection of quality Web site addresses. If our readers feel that this new innovation in the series is useful, we plan to provide a more extensive Web site section in each new book in the *Issues* series.

★ ★ ★ ★ ★

Friends of the Earth (UK)
http://www.foe.co.uk
The effects of changing weather patterns are set out, as are policies to cut climate changing pollution. Outlines steps that can be taken by individuals to avoid the effects of changing weather patterns like El Nino. A free information pack is available Spring '98.

Greenpeace
http://www.greenpeace.org.uk
Recent climate change press releases. Newsbriefs of particular interest include a challenge to industry's account of climate change and a positive view of the Kyoto conference. A good source for current news reports and general background information.

Meterological Office (UK)
http://www.met-office.gov.uk/
Climate change can be found under Research, Development and Operations on the home page. This includes data from the Hadley Centre for Climate Predication and Research, with specific reference to the impacts of climate change, comments on the Kyoto conference, and a Global Warming Gallery. Historical temperature records, seasonal forecasts and predictions on future climates are also given. Gives a glimpse into the past, present and future impacts of climate change.

The European Science and Environment Forum
http://www.esef.org
Links to World Climate Report, a publication covering the science and politics of global climate change. Current issue (Vol. 3, no. 11) discusses hurricanes, cyclones, El Nino and provides a monthly temperature update.

The Intergovernmental Panel on Climate Change (IPCC)
http://www.ncdc.noaa.gov/ol/climate/climateresources.html)
A link to peace, environment, human rights and development groups on the Internet. May take time to sift through general information for specialized topics.

United Nations Environmental Programme (UNEP)
http://www.unep.ch
– and – http://www.unfcc.de
Has a climate change information kit which includes numerous factsheets on the greenhouse effect and changing weather patterns.

Climatic Research Unit
http://www.cru.uea.ac.uk/cru/data
The Climatic Research Unit (CRU) is widely recognised as one of world's leading institutions concerned with the study of climate change. More suited to further education students and academics.

ACKNOWLEDGEMENTS

The publisher is grateful for permission to reproduce the following material.

While every care has been taken to trace and acknowledge copyright, the publisher tenders its apology for any accidental infringement or where copyright has proved untraceable. The publisher would be pleased to come to a suitable arrangement in any such case with the rightful owner.

Introduction

An introduction to climate change, © Information Unit for Conventions, United Nations Environment Programme (UNEP), *The main culprits*, © World Energy Council and DTI, 1996, *Key findings*, © The Met. Office, December 1997, *Climate change*, © Natural Environment Research Council, *The problem in a nutshell*, © WWF, *The issue of winners and losers*, © Information Unit for Conventions, United Nations Environment Programme (UNEP), *1997 – a year of weather extremes*, © Friends of the Earth, *The very model of a global argument*, © The Independent, December 1997.

Chapter One: The Effects

Potential effects of climate change in the UK, © Global Climate Change Information Programme, *Warmer weather brings threat of malaria and cholera*, © The Independent, September 1997, *Long range weather forecast: hot, dry and French*, © The Guardian, July 1996, *An iceberg on tap*, © The Daily Mail, September 1997, *Potential impacts on the countryside*, © Countryside Commission, *Big question of survival*, © The Guardian, December 1997, *Could global warming sink your holiday plans?*, © The Independent, November 1997, *Britain calls for US action on climate*, © The Independent, October 1997, *Global warming poses new threat to whales' survival*, © The Independent, June 1997, *Birds of a weather*, © The Daily Mail, August 1997, *The biggest thaw*, © WWF, *Global warming*, © Young People's Trust for the Environment and Nature Conservation (YPTENC), *Wildlife drowning under the high seas*, © The Independent, August 1997.

Chapter Two: Seeking Solutions

The planet's hottest problem, © The Guardian, October 1997, *Carbon dioxide emissions since 1800*, © IIASA, *Now the test for Kyoto resolution*, © The Independent, December 1997, *Is the Government's target for greenhouse gas just so much hot air?*, © The Independent, December 1997, *All that Kyoto heat, for next to nothing*, © The Independent, December 1997, *WWF's climate change campaign*, © WWF, *The world in 2050*, © United Nations, *The DIY guide to combating global warming*, © Ark Campaigns Ltd, *The future of the climate*, © Andrew Goudie, 1997, *A global inventory of first physical impacts of climate change*, © WWF.

Photographs and illustrations:

Pages 1, 12, 26, 31, 39: The Attic Publishing Co, pages 3, 13, 19, 30: Ken Pyne, pages 9, 17: UNEP.

Thank you

Darin Jewell for assisting in the editorial research for this publication.

Craig Donnellan
Cambridge
April, 1998